D1497912

The Best of Greg Clark & Jimmie Frise

The Best of

Greg Clark & Jimmie Frise

STORIES BY GREGORY CLARK

PICTURES BY JAMES FRISE

COLLINS · TORONTO · 1977

This selection first published 1977
by Collins Publishers
100 Lesmill Road, Don Mills, Ontario

© 1977 Toronto Star Syndicate

All rights reserved. The use of any part of this publication reproduced, transmitted in any form or by any
means, electronic, mechanical, photocopying, record-
ing, or otherwise, or stored in a retrieval system,
without the prior consent of the publisher is an in-
fringement of copyright law.

Design: Harold Boyd

Canadian Cataloguing in Publication Data

Clark, Gregory, 1892-1977.
The best of Greg Clark & Jimmie Frise

Selections taken from stories appearing in the
Star weekly, 1930-1942.

ISBN 0-00-216683-6

I. Frise, James, 1891-1948. II. Star weekly,
Toronto, Ont. III. Title.

PS8505.L32A6 1977   C818'.5'2   C77-001534-4
PR9199.3.C52A6 1977

Printed in Canada

The Stories

Introduction

Every Saturday, back about 40 years ago, Canadians all across the country waited eagerly for the old *Star Weekly*. And the thing they read first was the further adventures of Greg Clark and Jimmie Frise.

The stories selected for this book—and the hundreds more that appeared in the paper over more than 10 years—became so famous and popular, that anyone who lived here in the 1930's will always think of Greg and Jimmie as "family".

The funny kind of things that happen in the stories are no different from what happens to all the rest of us. But when Greg put it down in words and Jimmie drew the picture, a special magic took over and these everyday events radiated a warmth and friendliness that made everybody happy.

The famous team of writer and illustrator was born almost by accident. In the Depression of the 30's, all the newspapers, the *Star Weekly* included, were full of doom and gloom. But the *Star* did have one bright spot, a cartoon drawn by James Frise called Birdseye Centre, a little town that had never heard of hard times. In response to the cartoon's popularity the paper wanted something else that was optimistic and happy, Gregory Clark, a young man who was building a solid reputation as a reporter, agreed to write a story a week to be illustrated by James Frise. And there it was—perfect from day one.

Here is a collection of The Best of Greg Clark and Jimmie Frise, created between 1934 and 1939. The stories are as fresh and enjoyable today as when they first appeared.

*The following stories originally appeared in
the* Star Weekly *on these dates:*

WEASELS – September 7, 1935
NUTTING – October 12, 1935
GOOD SAMARITANS – May 2, 1936
UNACCUSTOMED AS I AM – August 29, 1936
MUSHROOMS – September 5, 1936
MIRACLES – December 21, 1935

Weasels

"**L**OOKIT," said Jimmie Frise, "that fruit!"

We were doing forty along the highway, and every farm had its roadside display of fruits and vegetables.

"Beautiful, Jimmie, beautiful," I agreed. "At this season of the year, is anything in the world lovelier than a great big fat double-chinned, ripe, red, home-grown tomato?"

"And peaches, look," said Jim. "Forty cents."

"They're nice on top," said Jimmie, "but look at these underneath!"

16

"Keep your eye on the road," I warned him. "I'll give you a play-by-play account of the fruit stands as we go by."

"You know," said Jimmie, "I wonder at the farmers of Ontario going to market at all. Here they have a million-dollar pavement running right past their doors. Then they have a quarter-mile of shop front in their fields all along the highway. Why don't they just set everything they grow out on the side of the highway and make the buyers come to them?"

"A good idea," I agreed

"Instead of hauling their stuff miles and miles to a town," pursued Jim, "at some expense of gas and wear and tear on their truck; and instead of going into a town where they are at a disadvantage, why don't they draw the buyers on to their own ground, where the buyers are at a disadvantage? In town, at the market, the buyers know the prices prevailing. They know just how much produce is on hand. They have the upper hand of the poor farmer. But if the farmers just set their stuff out on the highway along their own property, and the buyers had to come out and compete with one another, the farmers would get better prices, the dealers would have to buy quick, for fear some other dealer is cornering the supply — you can see how it would go?"

"Why don't you suggest that to the farmers?" I asked. "It's a swell idea. Makes the world come to the farmer instead of the farmer coming to the world."

"I don't know," said Jim. "I sometimes think only the innocent and gentle people are left on the farm. A sort of natural selection has been going on this last fifty years. All the shrewd people, the weasels, the wise guys, the smarties, have left the farms for the towns and cities. Gradully, year by year, the process has thinned out all the sharp-witted ones, and now only the kindly, slow-going, honest people are left on the land. The way they let the city dwellers put it over them seems unexplainable to me, except by the theory that they are too gentle in their spirits to struggle against city weasels."

"Like us?" I asked.

"Yes, like us," stated Jim. "Even we try to put it over country people whenever we deal with them. I bet you if we stopped along here to buy a basket of apples, we'd chisel the price and we'd pick the best packet, and fiddle and fume, as if we were buying a house and lot. Yet do you realize what the farmer gives us for forty cents?"

To Haggle and Pry

"He gives us," declaimed Jimmie, "the patient toil of years, the clearing of his land, the plowing, and the planting of little apple trees. He gives us all the patient years of waiting for the trees to become big enough to bear. Years and years of patience that is utterly unknown to-day in any other industry. Then at last, after he has plowed among them, and sprayed them and pruned them, and watched and tended them, at last they bear. And he sprays them again and guards them. Then he performs the last joyous rite of climbing ladders and picking these apples and selecting them and basketing them — and he sells them to us for forty cents!''

"You don't think of that," I admitted.

"No," cried Jim. "Yet when we stop to buy a basket of apples, we sort and pick and shift the baskets around, and mumble forty cents, forty cents, to ourselves, doubtfully, hoping he'll say thirty-five to you, mister. We're weasels, that's what we city folk are, just weasels."

"And what's more," said Jim, "I think we ought to stop along here somewhere and pick up a basket or two of apples. At this season of the year, every Canadian ought to bring home a basket of something every day. This is the harvest home. As an act of grace, every Canadian ought to bring a basket of God's bounty home every day, so long as the harvest lasts."

"Hear, hear," I applauded, watching eagerly ahead for a good roadside stand.

We passed a couple of small ones where there didn't seem to be much of a display. Then a fine big show loomed up.

"Ah," said Jim. "Here's the one. A real enterprising fellow, this."

He had a wooden stand, like a counter, with the baskets set on cleats so they leaned outward for the inspection of the passers by.

We slowed down and got out.

A small dark man, who looked more like a city slicker than a farmer, rose to greet us.

"Apples," he said, "fifty cents, these and those are sixty. Green tomatoes fifty. Gherkins, sixty "

"Mmmm," said Jimmie, examining the baskets. "Apples fifty, eh?"

"Now, now, Jim," I protested.

"Well, I only mean," Jim hastened; "they've been forty cents all along the road." "These are choice," explained the little dark man. "These are all hand-picked. No fallen goods here. Look, the quality, mister. Look at those silver onions? Did you ever see peas in a basket better sized?''

Jim scooped a handful, revealing larger ones beneath.

"They're a nice size on top," said Jim, "but underneath, look!"

"Jimmie," I protested hotly. "What were you saying only five minutes ago? I thought you weren't going to haggle and pry and fiddle."

"I'd let that basket go for fifty cents," said the little dark man. He was looking at his watch.

Buyers Become Sellers

"Come, Jimmie," I said, "the gentleman is perhaps getting ready to close up shop. Do you want any apples or don't you?"

"I was looking for snows," said Jim.

"They won't be on the market for a month yet," said the little man, shortly. He again looked at his watch.

"It seems funny to me" I explained to the little man. "My friend and I here were only five minutes ago discussing you farmers, thinking how you are chiselled and set upon by us city people."

"It's a fact," admitted he.

"And yet here, the first thing, we are complaining about your goods," I laughed, "and trying to get a lower price."

"It's a fact," said the little man, gazing up the road as if expecting somebody.

"I suppose you sell quite a bit in a day, though?" I chatted, since Jimmie was still gloomily picking up this basket and that and setting them down and looking below the top layers of apples.

"I haven't sold one dollar'd worth all day," said the small man, grimly. "Not one dollar. People stop and look and drive off. They are all buying to a price. To save five cents, they will drive thirty miles. Huh."

"It must be pretty trying," I said, "seeing this stuff that you have planted and nurtured and grown so patiently, being sniffed at by strangers."

"It's a fact," agreed the little man. "Have you gentlemen five minutes to spare?"

"I suppose so," I said.

"I'm expecting a lady coming to my place to supper; I think she must have gone to the wrong place. Would you mind tending my stand here for five minutes while I go and make a call?"

"Why," said Jim, "all right. We might change your luck. Will we sell, if anybody comes, or just hold them till you return?

"Sell," said the little man, walking over to Jim's car and

leaning in to look at the dashboard. "You haven't got the right time, eh?"

"I haven't a clock," said Jim. "All right, we'll see if we can't do some salesmanship for you."

The little man walked back the lane towards the farm house.

Jim and I stood, in businesslike attitudes, in front of the stand, looking with expectant air at each car that whizzed by. Some of them slowed. One of them stopped while a large, surly, sow-like lady in expensive clothes leaned out the window of the car and stared wordlessly at our exhibit.

"Puh," she said, and drove on.

"I don't mind if he takes his time," said Jim. "I rather like this. Isn't it a funny feeling, having something to sell? You don't realize how different a feeling it is, buying and selling. I feel all this stuff is wonderful, now. A few minutes ago, I thought it was lousy."

A truck with two men came along and slowed.

"Buyers," hissed Jim. "Dealers."

The man at the wheel called out:

"How many apples you got?"

"Eleven baskets," I answered smartly.

"How much?"

"Fifty cents."

The two men got off, and looked our display over. Eleven of apples, six of gherkins, five green tomatoes, four of green onions, three plums, three crab apples, and some sundries.

"We'll take the lot," said the dealer. "Figure it up."

Something Pretty Funny

He drew out a wad of soft one-dollar bills and wet his thumb, while Jim started to count up. The other man began lifting the baskets on to the truck, and I helped him.

So while we rapidly loaded the stuff on to the truck, Jim did his adding first by mental arithmetic and then by pencil and paper. And he was just finishing it on paper when the man I was helping threw up the back of the truck with a bang.

"O.K.," he sang out.

"O.K.," said the other man, taking two strides and swinging aboard the truck.

"Hey," Jim and I yelled.

The truck roared and lurched on to the highway.

"Get the number," screamed Jimmie, darting out on to the road.

But to both our astonishments, there was a potato sack

hanging down at the back which totally concealed the license plate.

"Oh, oh, oh," we said to each other.

And out the lane came the little dark man.

He halted in amazement, staring at the poor bare wooden rack where his fruit had been. Fruit of his toil.

"Where the...?" he asked.

So we explained it to him.

"But didn't you get their truck number?" asked the little sad man, spreading his hands pitifully.

"There was a sack over it," we told him.

"Couldn't you identify it no way?"

"It was too sudden, and anyway, we didn't want to leave without explaining to you," said Jim.

"Well," he said, "where do I get off?"

"It was our fault," I stated.

"I asked you to mind it, though," said the small man timidly.

"There you go, Jimmie," I pointed out. "See, he wants even to take the blame. You were right about country people. They are too gentle, too innocent."

"I'd take half the blame," put in the small man.

"That's fair," we agreed.

So Jim showed us his figuring, and it came to seventeen dollars and forty cents. We paid nine dollars to the little man. Four-fifty each, which I borrowed from Jim.

"Gentlemen," said the small man, "you are both very kind. You have no idea how this would ruin me."

"We want you to know," I explained, "that we both have the deepest respect for the farmer."

"Well, you excuse me please." said he. "I have to catch the bus."

A bus was snoring towards us, at a little distance.

"Wait," yelled Jim, as the small man started to run down the highway, "we'll give you a lift."

But he paid no attention, ran swifly two telegraph poles down, signalled the bus and piled aboard it.

"Now that's a funny one." said Jim. "That's a real funny one."

We stood looking after the bus. Then we looked at the skeleton of the fruit rack. Just a poor little jimcrack thing it was now, bereft of its glowing baskets.

"Somehow, I don't like that," said Jim, scratching his head and looking in down the lane at the small farm house crouching amidst the lilac bushes.

We got in the car. Jim reached for the key on the dash. Then he fumbled in his pockets.

"The key, the key," he suddenly yelled.

"What?" I asked.

"The key," he yelled again. "Did you see anybody touch the key?"

"The little man leaned in to see the time on the dashboard," I said.

"Oh, oh, oh," said Jim, leaping out of the car. "Come into the farm!"

The little farm house was all still. No dog. Nobody in the kitchen, with its open door.

"Hello," we called.

"Milking," said Jim, heading for the barn.

We found a lady in a straw hat, milking cows.

"Oh," she said rising. "Are you the gentlemen for the keys?"

"Yes," cried Jim. "Did you..."

She reached into her apron pocket and handed Jim his car keys.

"I'll be..." I said.

"Who gave you the keys?" asked Jimmie politely.

"Don't you know him?" asked the lady, surprised. "I only know him as Jake."

"How did he happen to give you the keys?" asked Jim.

"Why, a few moments ago," she said, "he came to ask if he could use the phone to call his truck. and he handed me these keys and said a gentleman will be along presently to ask for them."

"Do you know this little man out in front of your place?" I put in.

"I only know he came last Wednesday," said the lady, "and gave me a wonderful talk about how poor we farmers are at selling, and asked if he could set his stand up on our front there."

"Is he a farmer?" I inquired.

"Pooh!" laughed the lady. "He's some sort of crack-brained fellow from the city. He brings his stuff out from the city every morning in a truck."

"Oh, oh," said Jimmie and I.

"But he's had his fill of roadside marketing," the lady laughed, preparing to sit down by the cow again. "He told me to-night we've seen the last of him."

"I guess we have," said Jimmie and I.

So we thanked the lady for our keys and drove home without buying any apples at all.

The more we struggled the lower
we dangled ... the goat curled his
lips in nasty fashion ...

Nutting

"**I** KNOW a man," announced Jimmie Frise, "who planted a walnut tree on his place thirty-five years ago. And now it is worth $50."

"Well, well" I confessed.

"And if he had only planted an orchard of walnut trees," went on Jim, "he would be a rich man to-day. Think if he had planted one thousand trees."

"Fifty thousand bucks," I deduced.

"It just goes to show you," taught Jimmie, "Wealth is all around us, if we only knew it when we saw it."

"Aw, well," I said. "Maybe if we planted a thousand walnut trees now and waited thirty-five years, by that time probably walnut furniture would be out of fashion. Nothing but modernistic steel furniture by that time, even in the museums."

"Anyway," admitted Jim, "thirty-five years is a long time to watch a tree grow, don't you think?"

"One of my ancestors," I told Jim, "when he first came to Toronto, went away out on the outskirts of the village and bought a boggy piece of land just about where the Yonge St. Arcade is now. He traded that, as time went by, for a nice big hunk of land away out in the country. Away out where Bloor and Bay St. is now, but it was so sandy he let it go and Jesse Ketchum got it. So he decided the way things were going, he had better go out to Markham township."

"Civilization kept tramping right on his heels," said Jim.

"No," I explained, "as soon as Markham township got too thickly populated, that is, when he had about two acres cleared out of a hundred, why he up and went to Lake Simcoe. He cleared a few acres there and then heard about Grey county, so he went on there. Then he died. I bet if he hadn't died, he would have gone right into the Pacific ocean."

"Don't be sore at him," pleaded Jimmie. "Probably you are passing up just as many bets as he did.

"But think," I cried, "if he had hung on to that bit on Yonge St. I'd be lousy rich today."

"You and who else?" demanded Jim.

"How do you mean?"

"How many other descendants has this ancestor of yours?" Jim asked.

"Yes, that's so," I agreed. "I have about forty relatives out of him."

"You see?" explained Jim. "It is no use making a fortune unless you only have one child. And make sure you tell him to have only one child. It is this awful fecundity of rich men that defeats them in the end. Be as smart as you like, your grandchildren divvy it all up and pooie, it's gone." "Rich men," I suggested, "ought to plant walnut orchards. Every year, plant another thousand new ones, depending on how good a year it has been financially. Soak your wealth away in walnut. Then, no matter how many descendants you have, there's something for them all."

A Road to Nowhere

"How come?" asked Jim.

"Well, for instance, your smarter and foxier grandchildren," I explained, "will own the orchards. But your duller grandchildren will be looked after by having the job of cutting them down, and working in the sawmill, see? A walnut orchard, properly planted and spread over a series of years, ought to attend to the various needs of all your descendants down to the fourth generation, by which time, you ought to breed another genius again, who will replant. And there you have the secret of perpetual wealth.''

"The motto of the modern world ought to be," said Jim, "what we have, we can't hold."

"That's true," I agreed. "Nearly a hundred years ago Emerson said, 'There is nothing new, there is nothing true, and nothing matters.' Hanged if I can see all this frenzy in the world to make money and get on top of what, I ask?"

"I'd like to get on top of about a bushel of beech nuts," said Jim. "All this talk about walnut orchards has got me a little nut conscious."

"I often take my family nutting, at this time of year," I said. "Beech nuts and hickory nuts. But mostly the beech nuts are empty. And we get the wrong kind of hickory nuts. A bitter kind of nut, they call it a pig-nut."

"You ought to take me," said Jim. "I'm a country boy. I know a pig-nut when I see it."

"Then let's take an afternoon off and the two of us go nutting," I said. "There is nothing in the world like a good beech forest to give a man that rich, old, nutty flavor in his spirit."

"As a matter of fact," submitted Jim, "there is no time of the year, not even the spring, as lovely in the country as right now. Nutting should be an institution in Canada. The country should be filled with family parties, their little picnic fires should be sending up their incense in the autumn haze."

Which poetry inspired us to immediate action and Jim locked up the office and away we went.

To find nut trees in the country is not easy. If you ask at wayside gas stations, as Jimmie and I did, they tell you they don't know of any, just the same as in speckled trout fishing. If you find a hickory tree near the highway, it turns out to be pig-nuts. If you see a beech grove in full view, it is one of those beech groves laden with empty shells.

"We have to get off the main roads, even the main side roads," Jim said. "Let's keep on until we come to a couple of ruts."

And in due time, we came, as always we do, to one of those concession roads that obviously leads nowhere. If you examine it carefully, you will see no trace of motor car tracks even a week old. Just a wagon track, as if the denizens of this particular concession only came out on Sundays. Up such a road you must go for nuts.

Nothing Just Like It

The fences up this lonely road were of two kinds—stump and boulder. Mighty men must have cleared this land. The stumps were grotesque and enormous. It took men, not horses, to struggle these giant octopi of pine into place. And maybe the men who heaved these rough walls of granite boulders into place may have had stone-boats to drag them. But no stone-boat could hoist them up into place.

"There were men hereabouts, once," I said.

"Nut-fed men," agreed Jim. "Nuts, they tell me, are the original and natural food of men. Back in the days when we were just losing our tails and still said hello when we met a monkey in the jungle, we ate nuts and insects, largely. A good big grasshopper and a handful of nuts was enough to carry a man ten miles on the trail of a mastodon."

"Not these sissy nuts you buy in stores," I pointed out.

"I mean wild nuts," said Jim, "with a tang. Butternuts, for example. That queer pungent, faintly bitter taste of a butternut. Is there anything quite like it in all the kindgom of flavor? Like celery, you can't describe the taste. And hickory nuts."

"I like beech nuts." I disagreed. "So delicate, so tender. I remember my family sent me a candy box full of beech nuts in the trenches. I ate them and the very next week we fought the battle of Passchendaele and drove the Hun back another two miles."

"Beech nuts are all very well for women and children," said Jim, "but I imagine a man fed on butternuts and hickory nuts would sort of be tanned inside and out, his muscles would get like rawhide. They have, I feel, a primitive effect on us."

"We'd start tree climbing again," I agreed. "It would rouse old instincts in us. Maybe we would start to grow tails."

Over the hill, a little old weather-beaten farm house came in view. Beyond it, the fields ended, and woodlots grew.

"Beech anyway," cried Jim. "And maybe hickory."

"The decent thing to do," I suggested, "would be to ask at the farm house. After all, nuts are a crop. They have a market value."

The farm house seemed half sunken in the ragged earth. The little barn at the back leaned awry, all to the east, as if the winds of the years had pushed it over. A couple of gnarled apple trees gestured in the front yard. No dog came forth.

We rapped, and an old man came to the door.

"Nuts?" he said, as if we had waked him from a long, long sleep. "There used to be plenty of them, I guess there still is. The best bush is in at the next corner."

"Does it belong to anybody?" we inquired.

"Oh, I suppose so. Nearly everything belongs to somebody,"

said the old man. ''But I wouldn't know who's got it now.''

''Well,'' we said, waving good-by.

At the next corner, indeed, was a bush. It was one of those dim and aisled beech woods that you rarely see except in paintings. The blue gray trunks of the beeches, the bare clean earth below them, made it seem a cathedral. A strong rail fence surrounded it.

Are They Yelling at Us?

''I see no signs,'' said Jim. ''I guess it is all right to go in.''

We parked the car, and over a rise in the narrow two-rut road came three ragged little boys on the run.

Like squirrels, they came, stopping and starting, darting into the wayside brush, peering at us. The largest one, about ten, clad in ragged little overalls and with a mane of yellow red hair, grinned from a distance.

''Hello,'' I said in my best boys' camp manner. ''Hello fellows. Would it be all right for us to in here and gather a few beech nuts?''

But the lad ducked into the brush, and the next we saw, he was with his two smaller companions, peering at us over some rocks, fifty yards back up the road.

''Humph,'' said Jim. ''Maybe your theory is right. They're more like monkeys. Perhaps they live on nuts.''

''To think,'' I said, ''that they are the get of the mighty men who made those stump fences and flung those granite boulders around.''

We climbed the rail fence and entered the beech forest. The very first low branch we found was laden with husks. The husks were bursting with large glossy beech nuts. And when we toothed open the first nut, lo, the shell was filled with downy yellow meat, plump as a roast chicken's breast.

''Yum,'' said Jim.

So we transferred everything out of our side pockets into our upper pockets and went to work. Jim found a long dead stick, with which he rattled up amidst the branches, and down came the showers of husks.

''The best way is to have a sheet on the ground,'' I said.

The three little boys had come furtively out of the brush, and were now climbing on to the top rail of the fence behind us. Cautiously, one by one, they took their box seats to watch us.

''Hi, fellows,'' I repeated, feeling they were getting friendlier. Their faces were split with grins.

''Apparently, in this forgotten corner of the earth, the sight of company is unusual," I said

"They sure are excited," agreed Jim, waving to them.

But we gathered nuts, and such nuts. Only the odd one was light and empty. Jim, like a true nutter, kept foraging deeper into the aisles of lovely beech, looking for the perfect tree. And finding it every minute or two, only to find a better one. We had got perhaps seventy-five yards into the woodlot when we heard all the little boys on the fence suddenly start a chorus of yelling.

"Are they yelling at us?" I wondered.

"I think they are calling a dog," said Jim.

From behind a beech tree, at this moment, stepped an animal.

"Goat," said Jim, munching.

"I never saw a dirtier one," I said. "I wonder if it is a nanny or a billy?"

The goat was standing stock still, staring at us. It had pale gray eyes, in which there was no expression at all. It nodded its head abruptly at us. It gave a kind of a snort. It lifted its face and curled its upper lip up over its nose in a very curious and disagreeable fashion.

"Goats," said Jim, "are something I know very little about."

The little boys had quit yelling, and I looked back to see them all perched on the fence, bending low, peering at us.

"Jim," I began.

But on the dry ground, I heard Jim's feet. And without bothering to give the matter any study, I started too.

The goat gained. It made snuffy little sounds with its every jump. It was a large, a shaggy, and grayish, and, as I found out, a foul smelling goat.

It took me first. And then it took Jim. I know more about it taking Jim than me. All I felt was a thump, which downed me while the little boys on the bleachers cheered. Without changing stride, it bounced, on curious stiff legs, after Jim and hit him foul, Jim went down very loosely.

"Second down," yelled the red-headed boy, for now we were only a few yards from them.

I got a beech limb. Thank heavens a beech tree kindly offers a limb low to the earth. The beech is a noble tree. I was unable, at the moment, to do more than get an elbow and cross-leg grip of the limb, suspended, you might say. The goat wheeled and reconnoitered me, thus allowing Jim time to do what I did.

He too hung suspended.

"Climb up on the limb," Jim cried. "Maybe he can jump."

"Climb up yourself," I retorted. "You dangle lower than I do."

But beech limbs are limber. And the more you struggle, the lower you dangle, and the goat snorted and curled its lip in that very nasty fashion. He would go and study Jim. Then he would wheel and study me.

"Boys," I called. "Hi, fellows! Whose goat is this?"

But the three boys shyly got down off the fence and stood, like wild things, on the edge of the wayside brush, ready to vanish.

"Fifty cents," yelled Jim, "if you call the goat away."

But all three vanished into the brush, and all we could see, though we raised the ante to two dollars, were little shaggy heads coming and going, like African pygmies, in the thickets.

And mouths bright with grins.

"I can't dangle here much longer," I said to Jim.

"Now, if we had been eating nuts for a few months," said Jim.

"This is absurd," I granted. "The two of us hanging like monkeys. One of us should drop and make a run for it, and so let the other get to the fence. Then we could go and get help."

"Which do you prefer," asked Jim, "the run for it, or the dangle?"

"I'll dangle," I offered.

But the goat, apparently being feeble-minded and unable to keep his mind long on any one subject, suddenly decided to leave, and on quick-trotting feet, and head jerking his filthy beard under him, he sped away in the direction from which he had come.

And down we dropped, all in one breath moving from pre-historic to modern times, and raced for the fence and cleared it and got into the car.

"Ah," we sighed.

And, anyway, we wanted to see a man about a dog in Acton, so we went along.

Good Samaritans

"**A** HA," cried Jimmie Frise, "new neighbors."

He pointed up street, where a massive van was just backing before a vacant house.

"That house," I commented, "has been vacant for months and months. I wonder what they'll be like?"

"Probably," said Jim, "they'll have a large and vicious dog that will take six months to decide who he can lick along this block."

"Probably they'll have about six sniffly kids," I said, "all prone to

Jim hung the pictures while I unloaded our new neighbours' book boxes ...

whooping cough and mumps. We've been pretty lucky in this block for some years. I guess this is the end.''

"On the other hand," said Jim, "it might be a rich widow. Or maybe an elderly childless couple.''

"At that," I submitted, "it might be some fellow we'd grow very fond of around here. Maybe the kind of man who would raise choice roses and always want to be giving rose bushes to his neighbors.''

"By jove," said Jim, "he might be the kind of fellow who keeps a lawn rolled and one of those lawn-edging machines with a wheel on it.''

"I'd rather be optimistic about them, whoever they are," I agreed. "Because a neighborhood needs new neighbors every now and then. A neighborhood kind of gets tired of itself, doesn't it?''

"Sometimes the most sensational things," mused Jim, "happen as the result of a stranger moving into a community..The most incredible things. Lovers may change. Death may move in with that new neighbor.''

"Brrr,Jim" I said.

"In this new family," declaimed Jim, "may be a beautiful young girl who may be your future daughter-in-law. By such chances as this are romances born to our midst. On the other hand, who knows but this stranger may be the man of destiny, a man of ideas, who, as the months go by and he gets to know us all, may alter the lives of every one of us. Give us new and powerful ideas. Take us into partnership in some fabulous gold mine. It is just that way that fortune comes to us.''

"Jim," I said, "let's stroll up the street and see what kind of furniture they've got. Get an idea of what they amount to.''

"Maybe this stranger," said Jim, "is a villain. Maybe at this moment, while only the moving van stands there before a vacant door, maybe already tragedy and disaster have come to this street. Maybe he will be a robber of widows and orphans. Maybe he will run off with somebody's wife.''

"Let's got and take a casual look at their furniture," I suggested anxiously, "If I don't like the look of their stuff I'll take darn good care not to let this bird chum up to me.''

Jim got slowly to his feet, so heavy were his ideas.

"The moving in of a new neighbor," said Jim, "is a momentous occasion. Is it any wonder, on moving day, that all the curtains of the world are stirring as curious ladies stand within studying each item of the new arrival's belongings?''

"It's not idle curiosity," I said, restraining Jim with my hand, so that he would stroll more slowly.

New Neighbors' Furniture

"I think it is the right of everybody," declared Jim, "to express some interest in new neighbors. Not only in self defence. But in order to offer a friendly and neighborly hand, if need be."

The van men were already, with that modern speed and efficiency moving men have developed, laying articles off the huge van. They spread burlap out on the lawn, and as Jim and I slowly approached they set down an entire dining room suite. It was of oak, massive and simple in design. It was decidedly impressive.

"I see no scuffs and footmarks on the legs of the chairs," I said in a low voice to Jim; "from which I deduce that there are no young children in this family."

As we walked past the van we glanced in.

"Mmm," said Jim, "very nice, very nice."

"Jim," I said eagerly, "I think I am going to like our new neighbors. Did you notice the quality of that walnut bed? It was genuine colonial or I'm a Dutchman."

We strolled up to the corner, paused a moment, and then started to stroll slowly back.

"Take it slow," I warned. "There is no harm in two gentlemen walking up and down their own street."

"See what's coming," hissed Jim. "A gun cabinet, isn't it?".

It was a gun cabinet. In hand-rubbed walnut, a tall, commodious cabinet with plate glass front and racks covered with red baize inside to support guns.

"Jim, I'm going to call on this new neighbor," I cried, "very soon and get a sketch of that gun cabinet. That's what I've wanted for years."

"Look," said Jim, as we drew nearer, "a real old walnut cupboard. Say, these new folks have taste."

The moving men were delicately lifting the huge old-fashioned cupboard, tall and massive, plain as a pail, charming as only old things can be. Jim and I halted to admire it.

"Easy, boys," grunted the boss moving man. "This is one of the pieces the dame was so excited about."

They eased it to the pavement.

"I never saw a more beautiful walnut cupboard," said Jim. "Not a curly-kew, not an ornament or a scroll on it. Every line of it is beautiful. Boy, I wonder where that came from?"

The moving men hoisted it.

Jim and I continued, after a quick glance around at the articles on the lawn, to stroll past, while the men grunted and stumbled with short paces towards the house with the huge cupboard.

"Whoever they are," said Jim, "they're somebody."

Down street a little way we turned about and strolled back. The men had the beautiful cupboard to the front door and were clustered at the door, darting anxiously this way and that, the way moving men do when they are stuck. Loud voices shouted brief orders. The figures moved briskly, taking fresh holds of the huge cupboard.

"Let's give them a hand," I suggested. So Jim and I hurried up the walk and stood to.

"Here, boys," said Jim. "A couple of neighbors to the rescue."

"Lift from the bottom" called a breathless voice, "while I lower her over."

We seized hold and lifted tenderly. It was lovely to lay hands on that satiny old wood. Its deep patins, its gloss, modest but like a layer of richness over the glorious old brown wood, was a balm to the eyes as we leaned down close to it, almost pressing our cheeks against it.

"Eeeeaaaasy," said the voice. And in a moment, with four heavy steps forward, we had the lovely cupboard in the front hall of the vacant house.

"Thanks, gents," said the boss, amiably. "I'm much obliged to you."

"Just a neighborly act," I said.

"Call us if you need us again," assured Jim.

But we both had time to take a quick look around the empty house, noting the fine mantel and fireplace, the elegant though restrained decoration of the living room.

Thus Jim and I walked pleasantly back and forth in the bright afternoon, while the huge van continued to pour forth its treasures. There were walnut bookcases and decidedly custom-built bedroom suites. There was a perfectly magnificent chesterfield, with two matching easy chairs, upholstered in wine red. There were cases and cases of books and pictures, all carefully covered with burlap.

"I'd like to get a squint," I said, "at those books. You can tell more of a man by the books he keeps than by anything else."

"Unless it's his pictures," said Jim. "I'd like to see his pictures."

At this moment the boss of the moving men came to the door of the house.

"Gents," he called, "if you don't mind?"

We hurried up the walk eagerly.

"That big chesterfield," said the boss. "The dame wanted it

up in the sunroom at the back of the first floor up. I wonder ..."

"Certainly, certainly," we assured heartily.

They had the chesterfield half-way up the stairs to the turn, and there they were stuck.

"I don't see how it will go up," said the boss, anxiously. "She said she measured it and it would go up easy. I wish that dame were here."

"Patience does it," said Jim. "It's astonishing the things you can bend around a stairway."

We all took hold and we wiggled it this way and that, lifted, turned, twisted, shoved.

"That dame," sighed the boss moving man, heavily. "You might say all women are bad when it comes to moving. But this one is the worst I ever saw. And where is she?"

"You'd think people with stuff like this," I said, as we all rested to have a cigarette on the stairway, "would be on hand to see it arrive."

"Why," cried the boss, angrily, "she said she would be here ahead of us. She drove away in her car ahead of us. Women like her give me a pain in the neck."

"Maybe she had a flat tire," I suggested.

"I wish she had," said the boss. "For one thing, she spent about a month arranging this move. She's been down to the warehouse at least six times in the past two weeks. She looked me and my boys over, as if we was candidates for the church or something. Our moral character. And did you ever, boys, hear anybody like her when we was loading this stuff?"

"Never, boss," chorused his three helpers.

"And now, when we're stuck, where is she?" demanded the boss.

Keeping Their Tempers

"It'll go up," I assured them.

And we took a new grip on the chesterfield and hoisted. And turned over. And turned up on end. And turned upside down. And grunted and sweated and kept our tempers nicely, the way moving men do.

And at last Jim, on a particularly strong shove, had the left rear leg of the chesterfield come off in his hand.

"My, my," we all said. And then the chesterfield went up as slick as a whistle. When we got it back in the big sunroom Jim said:

"I'll fix this leg on some way, boys, while you are getting the stuff in."

"Okay," said the boss; "I don't mind if you're here when she arrives. She may take it from a neighbor when she wouldn't from us.''

We worked on the chesterfield as the boys slowly and patiently carried up beds and springs and dressers and chests of drawers. Chests of drawers that would make your mouth water. Walnut and colonial, with the genuine look.

And while Jim struggled with the leg of the chesterfield I started arranging bookcases and tables that the men laid down in the big sunroom.

I unrolled a rug. I set the writing table along by the window. From one of the crates of books I took a few armfuls, and placed them artistically in the shelves of the bookcase. The former tenant of the house had left picture nails in the walls and, more because they were unsightly than that I wanted to see the pictures, I undid one of the boxes and took out some pictures.

"Jim," I cried, "look at this water color. Isn't that a beauty?"

Jim got up off the floor and came and helped me hang pictures.

"We may not have these pictures in the right place," said Jim, "but it is a neighborly thing to do to get them up somewhere anyway. They give such a homey look don't you think?"

Jim hung the pictures and I unloaded the book boxes and stacked the books in the bookcases. There were books on law and sets of novels, the works of Parkman; there were a large number of quite old editions of the poets, Longfellow and Wordsworth, and so forth.

"The new neighbor," I said to Jim, "has a pretty nice taste in books. I think he is a lawyer."

"A lawyer," said Jim, busy with a large etching, "will be a nice addition to this street."

I set vases in the window sills and spread an Indian rug over the writing desk.

"There," said Jim, standing back. "How's that?"

"Lovely, Jim," I cried. "This is surely the most curious thing. A true, old-fashioned house warming. Think of having neighbors that would come in and arrange your house for you."

"While we're at it," I said, "we might as well fix up another room. We may not get it the way she wants it, but it will be a great help to have the stuff laid out."

So we went and did the bedroom next. This woman was certainly a good manager. With chalk she had marked every piece of furniture, every picture, every single item large and small, with the position of the room it was to go in. This made it easy for Jim and me. We set up the bed. This is always an awful task.

Sometimes it takes half an hour just to assemble the side boards to the ends with those dizzy bolts that don't fit and everything.

We untied the mattress and laid on the springs, hung pictures, opened a case full of ornaments, doilies, objects of art, which I left to Jimmie's instinct to place artistically around on the dresser and tables.

The boss and his boys were still patiently climbing and descending, bearing their burdens. They looked in at us and smiled.

"A blame nice neighborly idea," agreed the boss.

We had just finished the master bedroom and were just in the act of surveying the other bedroom across the hall when we heard a harsh female voice screaming down at the front door. We listened

"You fools," said the voice, and meant it, "I've been hunting all over the city for you. What are you doing here? This isn't the house! This isn't the street! It's only an hour until dark. Get that stuff back into the van!".

"Jim," I whispered, "the back stairs."

Jim led. Tip-toe.

As we went down the back stairs we heard a kind of war party coming up the front stairs. And the lady was still screaming.

"You stupid asses," she yelled. "Why didn't you look at the paper I gave you? Why didn't I lead you by the noses first and show you the place? Would I live in a joint like this? You crazy, you, you, you."

By which time Jim and I were going out the back door; and at that instant we heard a terrible shriek which sent us at a fast jack rabbit canter out the side drive and across the street.

So we went and sat in Jim's parlor window, behind the curtains.

"How do you suppose the key those moving men had would fit the wrong house?" I trembled.

"When cock-eyed things like this happen," groaned Jim, "the key always fits. Or maybe the boys had a skeleton key. They usually have."

So we sat, long into the dusk, watching the boys carry out the stuff and pack it back into the van.

And the lady, whenever she appeared at the door, looked both busy and angry.

And when dark fell the van rolled away.

"Mmmmm,mmm," said Jim. "No neighbors yet."

Unaccustomed as I am

"**O**UR wives," said Jimmie Frise, "I suppose, are wondering what mischief we are up to. Every weekend when I go to the cottage, the first thing they ask is, 'Well, what's new? What mischief have you been up to?'".

"Those are the very words," I cried, 'that greet me. Alas we poor summer bachelors."

"I'm just as happy they don't know," said Jim, "how dull a time we have. Let them have a good time, with carefree hearts, is what I say."

"Isn't life dreadfully dull for men

Jimmie leaned forward and rested his fingers on the table. "Aw-wah, um. Er, ah, aw-wah," he began ...

of our age?'' I said. ''We are a little too old to make whoopee, and not old enough to enjoy sitting on a chair resting.''

''If we do cut up a little bit,'' said Jim, ''everybody says, 'Look at the old fools.' And if we don't cut up, everybody says, 'What's the matter with those guys? They don't know they are alive'.''

''Forty,'' I pointed out, ''is called the dangerous age. It certainly doesn't feel dangerous to me. Unless they mean you are liable to get hit by a car when you are forty, crossing the street.''

''I think,'' said Jim, ''that some poor guy of forty once said that to some girls, to try to appear romantic. And it's stuck ever since. Like a lot of other dizzy remarks.''

''Such as,'' I said, ''It's the humidity.''

''What gets me down,'' said Jim, ''being alone in the city, is the eating . . . I can't find anything I want to eat.''

''Why don't you eat at home?'' I asked. ''Get your own meals.''

''The dishes,'' said Jim.

''It's the beds that bother me,'' I said. ''I sleep in my own bed until the sheets and everything finally slides all off on the floor. Then I try my mother-in-law's. After I have kicked it all to pieces, I try my children's, one after the other. Finally the house looks so dreadful, I hate to go home. I sneak in along about midnight and don't turn on the lights, even.''

''And watering the garden!'' sighed Jim. ''Is there anything more tedious than watering the garden? What for? You plant the garden and the family is gone for the summer before anything blooms. The whole thing is burned to a cinder before they get home. So what the heck!''

''Laundry is bad, too,'' I pointed out. ''You lay a bath towel on the floor and pack on to it all the soiled shirts, socks, underwear, hankies, and take the thing to the laundryman. You forget to call for it, and wake up with no shirts, no anything. Sometimes, I get so muddled and helpless that I just sit in the nude in the middle of the whole mess and give up. Sometimes I am terrified in these hot spells that I might crack under the strain and drive down to the office with no clothes on. If I ever do, look after me, will you, Jim?''

''Ah,'' said Jim, ''if our womenfolk only knew what we sacrifice to let them go away for a summer!''

''I think,'' I declared, ''that we are entitled to some diversion. I don't suggest whoopee. But surely there is something we thousands of summer bachelors could do to break the monotony."

"On the way down this morning," said Jimmie, "I drove past a big house where they were getting ready for a garden party. Men with trucks were setting up colored marquee tents. Ladies were furiously busy around the big garden, with tables and chairs and benches."

Going to a Garden Party

"A garden party," I smiled, remembering my youth. "I had forgotten garden parties."

"We could go to garden parties," said Jim, "without losing our respectability. I read the sign they had up. It was a church garden party, I think, in aid of the Ladies' Frantic Endeavor, or something."

"It would be dull, maybe," I said.

"There would be great big glass bowls," recited Jimmie, "full of pale green lemonade, with hunks of ice floating in it. There would also be huge tanks of iced tea."

"I remember," I whispered. "And long tables."

"Tables covered with white table-cloths," sang Jim, "laden with plates of sandwiches of every sort, ham, with and without mustard; cress sandwiches and pepper grass sandwiches, rolled up; pickle and paste sandwiches; cookies and cakes and tarts."

"Rhubarb tarts," I said. "I remember one time, long ago, I went to a garden party and they had little rhubarb tarts. In the ordinary tart shell, some lovely old lady had mixed up rhubarb and sugar and egg to make a kind of filling, and it had a brown crust sort of cooked on to the rhubarb. I ate eleven of them."

"Maybe," said Jim, "this might be one of those garden parties where they would have a cold buffet at the back end, with a butler slicing boiled ham and the white meat of chicken."

"And all this amidst a garden of flowers," I cried, "with young ladies strolling slowly this way and that."

"You forget," said Jim. "Young ladies don't stroll this way and that any more. If there are any girls there - that means anything under fifty - they'll be sitting on the backs of benches or rolling on the grass in shorts, or flinging cakes at the butler."

"Jim," I asked, "whereabouts did you see this garden party in preparation?"

"Out our way," said Jim. "Admission 25 cents, in aid of the Ladies' Frantic Endeavor. Commencing, if I recollect, at 4 p.m."

"Let's go," I said. "Let's be neighborly, and go. At this time of year, they won't get many people. And like all enthusiastic ladies, they will provide far more than is needed. We could fill up with home-made food. That would be a blessing. Maybe they would have cucumber sandwiches?"

"I don't like cucumber sandwiches," said Jim, "they are so soggy. I like a good moist ham sandwich, with a taste of smoke cure. And a whiff of mustard."

"It's the duty of a citizen," I said, "a good citizen, to take an interest in these local social activities like garden parties. Maybe they might have a rummage sale, at the same time?"

"A garden party isn't only eating," agreed Jim. "They might have games, like cocoa-nut shies and things."

"I like those rummage sales," I confessed. "You can get all sorts of things. One time at a rummage sale I got a patchwork quilt that was my favourite for years."

"How will four o'clock catch you?" asked Jim.

But it was half-past four by the time we got away from downtown. And nearly five by the time we drew up and found a parking space in a handsome street of nice big homes. There was little space to park, so many were the cars.

"H'm," said Jim. "If I'd known it was going to be this popular, I'd have come earlier. I bet all the ham sandwiches are gone."

Signs of Excitement

We strolled up the street, seeing ahead many ladies clustered around the gateway of the fine house where the garden party was. There was music, which we later found came from a string orchestra concealed in the garden. As we drew near, I saw through the shrubbery that there were crowds of people in the garden, nearly all of them ladies. And sure enough, the whole place was laid out with tables, laden with the most delectable food and huge glass bowls, and girls were wandering all through the throng, with trays of stuff.

"Jim," I said, "I feel a little embarrassed. There's darn few men in there."

"We'll be all the more welcome," said Jim, craning his neck to look over the iron fence and shrubbery to see the tables.

"Jim," I insisted, "maybe it's a congregational affair. Maybe we have to belong to some church."

"Look at the sign," said Jim. " 'Public' it says. 'Admission 25 cents'."

The big white banner over the entrance said just that.

We dug out our two bits each, and advanced to the gate. The young lady at the table there, taking the money, looked at us keenly and excitedly as we paid our money.

"I don't think YOU have to pay," she said sweetly.

"Oh, by all means," said Jim, grandly, "by all means."

And we laughingly paid our quarters.

"Just a second, if you please," said the young lady, rising to her feet with every sign of pleasure and excitement. She whispered to another young lady who sped away in the crowd, and Jim and I stood, on one leg, as it were, just inside the gate, while the throngs of ladies looked at us pleasantly, though curiously, and we felt a little sheepish.

"I see sandwiches," muttered Jim, "that look mighty like ham to me. With old-fashioned lettuce sticking out the edges."

"Ah, green lettuce," I agreed. "Who on earth ever invented that tasteless, cabbagey head lettuce that they give us everywhere?"

"Mmmmm, green lettuce," said Jim. "With that faintly snappy lettucey flavor. Mmmmmm."

"I see," I said, leaning near, so that the ladies quietly watching us would think I was talking about the price of nickle or something big, "a large silver dish piled with those little round cakes with different colored icing outside and custard inside, I think."

"As for me," said Jim, lifting his chin and gazing with dignity out over the heads of everybody, "I think I see mint leaves floating in the iced tea."

"I wonder what the delay is?" I murmured.

But we wondered no longer, for three very stylish and excited ladies, with pale blue badges marked "Committee" came bursting through the crowd, with hands extended and seized Jimmie, he being taller and therefore more noticeable, and the oldest of them cried:

"How charming of you to come! Do come right this way! And is this your friend? Do come, won't you? This way."

And through the throng they pushed and shoved a lane for us.

"Welcome," said Jim to me. "I said they'd welcome us."

"A little too warm a welcome," I said, nervously, under Jim's ear as we pushed through.

"Men so seldom come to a garden party," replied Jim, "that it's an event."

And indeed I saw only two men beside us, and they were

elderly hen-pecked looking men with soft, tender faces.

We finally jammed our way through to a terrace at the back of the garden. Here it was not so crowded. A table and chairs were set out, and we were led there.

"My dear sir," said the head committee lady, "you will say a few words, won't you? You must say a few words, to start with."

Jim looked aghast at the lady.

"My friend here," he said, thumbing at me, "is the talker. Personally, I have little to say at any time. Specially in public."

"Ah," laughed the oldest one, her ah quivering up like a fire siren, "deeds, not words, is your motto!"

"Do you have any rummage sales?" I asked one of the other committee ladies, trying to break up this welcome and get going on more important matters.

"Rummage sales?" said the lady, quite shocked. She looked me up and down.

"Just a few words," cooed the oldest committee lady, leaning forward, coaxingly at Jimmie. "About your work."

"Work," said Jim, very embarrassed. He looked at me and then at the throng of ladies, all of whom were slowly crowding forward towards the terrace, and all with wide and interested expressions.

I rolled my eyes towards one of the tables we could still see; smacked my lips and then winked and nodded.

"A few words," I repeated.

"Please be seated," said the head committee lady to me, offering me a chair. "Ladies, we will stand in the rear."

She stepped forward, and held up her hand.

"Silence, please," she sang out in that clear ringing voice that comes with practice at many meetings.

Jnmmie stepped forward to the table and rested his finger tips on it. He was quite flushed. Jimmie is not a speaker. He hums and haws even when he is trying to buy a package of cigarettes. Resting on his finger tips and swaying away forward, then away back, and bending his head down to think, he said:

"Aw-wah, um. Er, ah, aw-wah. Oh, wah, ah. My friend here is fond of rummage sales. One time he got a patchwork quilt. As for me, er, ah, wah, oh. I prefer, ah, garden parties because of the sandwiches. Ha, ha, ha!"

I laughed merrily, but nobody else did. All the ladies looked surprised.

"We saw your sign up," said Jim, lifting his head and gazing far over the heads of the audience, "and being neighbors, and aw, wuh, oh, er, summer bachelors, you know how it is, why, er, ah, wuh, we thought it would be the neighborly thing . . ."

I heard a voice hiss in my ears.

"Isn't he Dr. McQuorquodale?"

I turned and looked into the wide and fierce eyes of the oldest committee lady.

"Dr. McQuorquodale?" I repeated.

"The missionary from Manchoukuo?" she hissed.

". . . drop in and do, er, ah, waw, justice," went on Jimmie, "to all these nice sangwidges - that is I should say sandwitches."

"No," I hissed fiercely back at the lady, "he is certainly not."

"Just a moment," she sang out instantly, in that loud, clear commanding voice of a president of committees. "There has been a little mistake. If you will pardon us for a moment, and continue with the refreshments . . ."

She took Jim's arm. Then she took mine. Above the elbow.

"Come this way," she said in a low tense voice.

The three other committee ladies were ganging us up from behind.

We were led rapidly over the fences to a sort of back gate, which was opened with a flourish.

"There," said the head lady. "Impersonators!"

"Impersa what!" I cried. "What is this? What's going on?"

"Fakers," said the head committee lady, pink with rage. "Making a fool of me."

"Madam," said Jim, "we are just a couple of neighbors who see a sign 'Public garden party, admission 25 cents'. Is it our fault? Did we pretend to be anybody? How did I know who you thought I was?"

"You might have known," grated the head committee lady, still so pink her powder showed, "when I led you to the table."

"Lady," said Jim. "I thought it was just a welcome you were giving a couple of gentlemen."

"Pawfff," said the lady, opening her little purse and handing me two quarters.

"Pawfff to you, madam," I retorted.

And we went to a Chinaman's and had chicken chow mein.

"Let's leave the rest of the mushrooms," said Jim "I feel a pain!"

Mushrooms

"**M**USHROOMS," said Jimmie Frise, "are now in season."

"For me," I replied, "mushrooms have no season. I like mushrooms on a nice rare steak. I like mushrooms on toast, soaked in their own butter gravy. But, most of all, I like mushrooms in June or January, February or December."

"But you admit," asked Jim. "that the best mushrooms are the ones you pick yourself in the woods and cook yourself, about nine p.m. at night at the conclusion of a

lovely September day out in the open, mushroom hunting."

"No, Jim," I said, "I can't say I do. As a matter of fact, I have never done that. But my feeling is, I prefer a good professionally grown mushroom that you can buy at any store to the wild article precisely as I prefer a nice piece of high grade beef to a hunk of wild venison."

"I thought you were a sportsman," sighed Jim.

"A man can be a sportsman," I explained, "and still like good food. If your idea of a sportsman is one who sits out in a frozen bog all day nibbling dry sandwiches and then comes in to a good meal of lukewarm canned beans and tea that would make your toes open and shut or float an egg, then I am not a sportsman. I like good edible tasty food, that's all."

"Good, edible tasty food," said Jim, "makes me think of a dull, sickening thud or something. It makes me think of fat men who live in furnished rooms all alone and go through life gently and silently staring at everything and nobody knows their name. Good tasty food. It makes me think of the kind of woman you describe as a great little housekeeper. Ugh."

"You like good food," I protested.

"Yes, but now and then I like a little adventure," said Jim. "I like to surprise my insides. Imagine being insides. Imagine spending your whole life at the mercy of somebody outside who does all the picking and choosing. And all you have to do every day of your life is receive a lot of guck, always the same, never anything new, never any excitement."

"Radishes," I pointed out, "onions."

"Pah," said Jim. "I believe in giving my insides a surprise every now and then. I like to go to one of these Italian restaurants and eat one of those great big soup platesful of rubbery spaghetti, four feet long, doused with meat sauce, red hot peppers, paprika and spices."

"So do I," I admitted. "Within reason."

"Reason nothing," said Jim. "You just ought to feel my insides when I start sliding that spaghetti down, all cool and smooth and hot and scratchy. Boy, my insides fairly shout with joy."

"A tall thin cold glass of water," I agreed, "often gives me that feeling of cheering."

"A tin dipper full," corrected Jim, "from a pump."

"I never really can enjoy a drink from a pump," I explained, "because of looking down the end of my nose for wrigglers or thinking of pollution."

Jim studied me for a long moment.

Men Who Lived Gloriously

"There is no thrill," said he, "like the wild thrill. No flavour like the gamey flavour. We are the flabby descendants of ages of men before us who lived gloriously on what they killed or picked up in the forest. It took us countless ages to arrive at roast beef and ham and eggs."

"During which time," I pointed out, "millions died in agony from eating the wrong thing."

"If you like," agreed Jim. "But certain things wake in us an ancient thrill, a sense of freedom, a feeling of reality, and among them are mushrooms and venison and partridges and speckled trout."

"Hear, hear," I confessed immediately.

"My suggestion is," said Jim, "that this week-end, we go mushrooming. This is the time of year. Mushrooms are to be gathered at all times of the year, from spring to autumn. But the autumn is the best time."

"How about toadstools?" I asked.

"There are only a few poisonous species," explained Jim. "And hundreds of edible species."

"Jim, if there were only the one poisonous species," I stated, "it would be too much."

"Wait a minute," said Jim. "I've got a government bluebook on mushrooms here somewhere. I'll show you how simple it is "

He hunted around through his files of old newspapers, straw hats, discarded suspenders, old snapshots he had lost for years, and so forth, the usual artist's files; and then he produced the pamphlet.

"See," he said, "it's got pictures. Here's one I've often eaten. Look. Deadly Agaric. No, no, not that one. That is deadly. Wait a minute. Here it is. See this lovely one. The Destroying Angel. No, no, wait a minute. That's the worst one of all. I've got its picture right here. Somewhere."

He thumbed through the pamphlet, showing me dozens of photographs of the worst-looking creations the Lord ever made. What day these flat, flabby, pallid things were made is not mentioned in the Good Book.

"Ah, here it is," cried Jim, exhibiting a dreadful bulbous-looking monster that seemed to have a skin disease. "This is the Shaggy Mane."

"Has it got hair on it?" I protested.

"Certainly not," said Jim. "That's a poetic name for it. Nothing in nature has such poetic names as mushrooms. My boy, I assure you once you have tried mushroom hunting you will become a mushroom hunter for life. In the cool September weather, in the early morning when everything is fresh and dewy, you go forth into the woods and along the margins of meadows, searching on the ground for these quaint little elfin creations of nature. They are white and cream and tawny brown. Pearly and bluish. They grow secretly in the shadow of trees, along the edges of old logs, in clusters where the long grass suddenly thins. In olden days, the people thought the fairies made mushrooms for chairs and parasols. They thought where the rings of mushrooms grew the fairies had been dancing."

"I wouldn't wonder," I said darkly.

"Mushroom hunting in September," declared Jim, "is as delightful a pastime as bird watching in May. Besides, you can't eat songbirds, but you can eat mushrooms."

"I might go with you," I said, "but only for the fresh air."

"Here," said Jim, turning to the government pamphlet again, "are the rules about how to avoid the poisonous species. Listen. It says, 'Avoid fungi when in the button or unexpanded stage; also those in which the flesh has begun to decay, even if only slightly, and those that contain larvae or worm holes.' "

"How delicious," I said

"Avoid all fungi which have stalks with a swollen base," continued Jim, "surrounded by a cup-like or scaly envelope, especially if the gills are white."

"It sounds like a snake and a fish combined," I declared.

"Avoid all fungi," declaired Jim, eloquently, "having a milky juice, unless the milk is reddish."

"Ah," said I, "reddish milk is O.K., huh?"

"Avoid all fungi," read Jim, "which have a bitter, unpleasant taste or an unpleasant odor."

"I'd be sure to like those," I agreed, "straight off."

"You see," said Jim. "Here it is, in cold type, perfectly plain and simple. We can't go wrong."

"I tell you, Jim," I said. "You collect mushrooms, and I'll collect poison ivy."

Baskets On Our Arms

But Jim is a man of imagination, and Saturday dawn he had me up and away to that country of beechwoods and pine and ash which lies amidst the limestone of Guelph and Georgetown, and across meadows soaked with dew we strode upward toward the skyline carrying baskets on our arms.

And sure enough, along the edge of a lovely beech wood we found in the meadow little encampments of the common mushroom. And I must confess that it was a pleasure to find them, and to kneel down and pick them, all firm and cool, and see how easily and crisply they broke apart, cap from stem. Jim and I soon had the bottoms of the baskets covered with them.

Into the woods we walked slowly, studying each tree trunk carefully, and finding amidst the pine woods the fluted stalk or Fall Morel, a curiously twisted and wrinkled thing like an old, old lady, but really only a day old; incredibly yellow coral fungi which Jim said were beautiful to eat, but which looked to me like asparagus gone to the dogs.

On dead trees we found flat fungi as red as Chinese lacquer, and in a quiet and lovely grove of birch trees, already fading to yellow, we came upon a lonely little thing of beauty, white as alabaster, curved and beautiful as a child's hand, rising like a dream out of the rotting earth mould. "And here," said Jim, proudly, "is my dear friend, Amanita Verna, the Destroying Angel. This frail and ghostly little plant has enough deadly poison in him to kill a tableful of guardsmen."

So we looked at it for quite a few minutes and thought of our poor ancestors who didn't have government pamphlets or any other knowledge, and then we kicked it to pieces and stamped on it, and wiped our boots on good wet meadow grass and went down afar to another beech-edged meadow to fill our baskets with the common mushroom.

Lunch we had with us in a box, and this we ate on one of those hills looking north across a thousand farms in autumn chintz. The afternoon we wasted splendidly turning up roads never seen before, and stopping at the gates of a hundred farms to see the apples on the trees, or observe the fat cattle or simply to try and guess what some distant farmer was doing. And usually we couldn't guess.

And through the afternoon haze we turned homeward for the feast.

"Now comes," said Jim, "the best part of mushroom hunting. Mushrooms are best the day they are picked."

And his family being on a picnic, we went to Jim's for the party. We sorted our baskets and set out only the choicest of our joint catch. Washed them, and dried them. Put on aprons.

Dedicated one whole pound of butter to the feast, and heated the big iron frying-pan.

"I'll fry," said Jim, "and you dance attendance on me. Heat the plates. Set the table."

"Bread?" said I.

"Would you eat a woollen blanket with pate de fois gras?" demanded Jim. "Just mushrooms. Nothing else. This is a feast".

And into the browning butter Jim sliced the plump mushrooms, where they swelled and curved and darkened and shrank. And on to a oven platter he ladled them out.

"Not done too much," he explained, "yet not underdone."

And, in due time, we had fried in butter enough of the succulent nubbins to make a fine black heap on two large plates and an odor so wild and strange and teasing as to make us almost perspire with expectancy.

"Fall to," cried Jim.

And we fell to, as only men who have been abroad in September can fall. And with our forks we ladled up mouthfuls of the hot and buttery darkness and found them as they should be, chewy, yet tender.

To tell the truth, right at the very start, I imagined I detected a faint bitterness. I did not like to say anything about it, because after all it was a feast and Jim was full of pride. But after I had got down about half of my pile, I slowed up a bit and looked at Jim. And to my horror, I caught Jim looking at me with a slight look of horror in his eyes.

"Do you - ah," I said, "detect a slight bitterness?"

"I do," Jim said, hallowly.

We pushed our plates away.

"How soon," I asked, huskily, "do the pains begin?"

"Sometimes," said Jim, in a thin voice, "not for two days."

We stared at each other. What a strange way for our long friendship to end. Boy and man, come Michaelmas, blame near a quarter century. And now a toadstool gets us.

"Jim," I said, "look through this basket here and see which of us is likely guilty. I would feel easier if I thought you had poisoned me rather than vice versa."

"Let's leave it," said Jim, rising sharply to his feet and clutching his stomach. "Here come the pains."

Sure enough, pains.

"Call a doctor," I commanded.

"No use, no use," said Jim. "I don't think there is a cure known for fungus poisoning."

"Will it hurt much?" I enquired.

"After all," said Jim, turning green, "does that matter?"

"You're quite right," I agreed, slipping back and getting a good grip of my central neighbourhood.

And then Jim's family walked in, loudly, gaily, full of picnic.

"What on earth," they cried, "are you cooking in that iron frying-pan?"

"Mushrooms," said we, concealing our agony bravely.

"Did you rinse it out, for goodness' sake?" they asked.

"No," said we.

"Well, it was full of laundry soap the last time I saw it," said the family, loudly laughing. "And that was this morning. That hasn't been a cooking pan for about ten years."

"We didn't eat any yet," said Jim. "We were just going to, when you came in."

"Ha, ha," said I. "Wouldn't that have been comic, if we had eaten any."

But Jim, looking at me, took me by the arm and led me out the back kitchen into the garden, under the stars, and we two walked up and down, pausing now and again, and walking up and down, along the back or bushy end of the garden, until nearly ten o'clock.

Miracles

"**N**INETEEN - FIFTY," muttered Jimmie Frise. "Twenty-one, twenty-four fifty, twenty-six".

"What's this?" I asked.

"My Christmas list," growled Jim, concentrating on a slip of paper. "Twenty-seven fifty, thirty-one forty, thirty-five. How horrible."

"Horrible what?" I inquired.

"How horrible," said Jim, angrily, "to be rating my loved ones and friends according to their price. Behold

"...ey", roared the stranger to ... world at large, "here's Ed ...ut."

me, in the name of Christmas, pricing my love and affection"

"Don't be silly," I laughed.

"It's tragic," declared Jim. "That's what it is. Just tragic. We make a list, carefully, we set down all the names of those from whom we expect presents. We go over it, pruning with the utmost exactness all names that might return a gift. Then we set opposite each name a price. Big prices for our immediate family, and getting smaller and smaller as we go down the list. Memory comes to our aid, as we recall what each one gave us last Christmas. We estimate the cost and value of that gift, and set it down as a working basis on our own list for this year."

"Nothing," I said, "is more embarrassing than to receive a Christmas gift from somebody you did not send one to."

"How horrible," cried Jimmie. "How unutterably horrible."

"Nonsense, Jim," I explained. "It's a convention. I can't think of any more sensible way of handling the Christmas giving than the way we do it."

"We should set apart ten per cent, of our Christmas funds," said Jim, "for giving anonymous gifts to people from whom we have no earthly expectation of receiving anything. Then it wouldn't be so wicked, this cold-blooded exchange business."

"I'm afraid this is a practical age, Jimmie," I demurred. "And mystical things don't happen."

"I believe," stated Jim slowly, "that there is some strange thing happens to all human hearts at Christmas. And I think it happens outside of all human control. Nothing makes me a true believer more than the strange miracle that occurs every Christmas to every sort and condition of men."

"You're romancing," I smiled.

Jim stood up and put on his coat.

"Let's go out," said Jim, "and prove it. Have you the afternoon? I tell you what we do. We'll fill the car tank. We'll drive down here to the lakeshore highway. At all the corners of the city streets leading into it, there are two or three or more men, hitch-hikers."

"Ah?" I said, getting up.

"Young chaps, with suit cases and white silk scarves," said Jim, "and gleaming smiles, thumbing their way home to some country town or village for Christmas. Older men, shabby, trying to get home for Christmas. Bums, too. Bums with nothing to redeem them in any man's eyes. Where are they heading, at Christmas?"

"Aha," I agreed.

"I'll show you," said Jim. "We'll pick up a bum. An oldish bum. A life-long flop of a man. A man without a single attractive or appealing thing about him. And we'll drive him where he is going, even if it takes all night."

"What if he's heading for Vancouver?" I asked.

"Be reasonable," huffed Jim. "We'll pick up this derelict, and we'll deliver him home. Not to the middle of some town. Not to a cross roads somewhere. But right to his door. And we'll so befriend him. He'll have to invite us in. We'll get into his house some way."

"And you'll show me this miracle?" I laughed.

"I'll show you this miracle," grinned Jim. "At random, deliberately picking every gamble against us, I'll show you this miracle."

"Probably," I snickered, as we went down the elevator, "they'll kick him out and sock us for bringing him home."

"Probably," said Jim.

"Or else, it will be some dumb little cottage in some dumb little village," I surmised, "and some dowdy old lady will say to him 'Hello, George' and she'll offer us a cup of tea."

"Probably," agreed Jim, heading out into the gray day and the threat of sleet.

"Because," I pointed out, "if you have a loafer in the family, you are never surprised to see him when he turns up."

"I'll show you," said Jim.

And we had the tank filled with gas, and Jim borrowed a couple of rugs from a friend's car, and we set out for the lakeshore highway.

Down the highway swept a wintry wind with sleet in it, and under the concrete bastions of the subways leading down from the city huddles of men stood, young and old, well dressed and shabby, with bags and bundles, signalling in the old fashion, and watching eagerly the outbound cars for a lift.

"Some miracle you'll show me," I said, as we coasted past the first corner and saw no one to fit our bill. "The only miracle will be Jim Frise giving some dull cluck a free ride home."

Jim coasted past the second subway. Five men stood there. But none were old, and none were ragged, and none looked like derelicts.

"We only have about three more spots where the hitch-hikers stand," I remonstrated. "And then we'll be outside the city."

"Keep watch," said Jim. "It'll happen. Around Christmas, it

always does."

"Heh, heh," said I.

We passed two of the remaining city streets touching on the highway. At one, a boy stood. At the other, two young chaps with those paper shopping bags. The last point was the Humber. And as, through the murk and wind, we came in sight of this last hope, there was no one at all waiting there.

"Ho, hum," said I.

"We'll go a little way out," said Jim. And drove on past the Humber and through the suburban villages westward, until we passed the golf clubs and before us stretched a lonely road, with shut cars snoring along, heads down homeward.

"So much for miracles," I said. "Where do we turn around?"

"We don't turn around," replied Jim. And I looked ahead, where his eyes were fastened, and saw a figure trudging by the side of the pavement.

Jim slowed as we drew near to it. It was, by the legs, an old man, for they were bent, and they picked themselves up and put themselves down the way the legs of old men do. He had no overcoat, but a leather windbreaker, and a heavy gray muffler high about his neck and ears. A battered fedora was drawn low.

"Maybe," said Jim, "he is only going up the road to the next farm. But something tells me not."

And with a last shove on the gas, he ran the car alongside.

"Mmmmm," said I.

For the face that turned up to us as we paused, was an unattractive face, the eyes were small and gray and cold in their expression, with red rims. The face was withered, and out of it stood a beaked nose. The mouth, hidden by a ragged white moustache, seemed only to be a slit.

After Long Absence

"Lift?" I called, winding down the window. "Thank you," said the old man. I reached back and opened the door for him and he got in back.

"Going far?" asked Jim.

"Far enough," said the old man.

"How far can we take you?" Jim requested.

"How far are you going?" the old man retorted. No smile broke the stoniness of his face. His bleak eyes regarded us levelly.

"We are not going any place in particular," said Jim. "We're out scouting around for some Christmas trees, so one way is as good as another.''

The old man studied us in silence. I nudged Jim on the leg.

''Going due Guelph way?'' the old chap asked finally.

''Sure,'' said Jim. ''I was just thinking about Guelph or somewhere even beyond there.''

''Stratford?'' inquired the old man.

''Stratford would be great,'' said Jim. ''Are you going to Stratford?''

''The other side of Stratford,'' said the old man, leaning back on the cushions, and loosening his muffler around his neck.

I twisted around in the seat to chat with him, but he was looking out the car window with that far away expression or lack of expression you see in people looking out train windows. He did not turn to face me. I saw his ancient boots, his patched trousers. His hands were knuckled and harsh.

''Have you come far?'' I asked.

''Province of New Brunswick,'' he answered, without turning from the window.

''Hitch-hiked?''

''Yes.''

I nudged Jim again. I was smiling to myself. Miracles. What a stuffy old stager this was for the manifestation of miracles. Between Clappison's Corners and Guelph, I got from him that he had not much luck at hitch hiking. That he had stood four days at Toronto's corners but finally had started on foot for Stratford

When we reached Guelph, he sat up and stared with great interest at the streets, the people, the busy pre-Christmas scenes.

''You've been away from Ontario a long time?'' I asked.

''Since 1920,'' said he.

''You were born up here?''

''Born and raised and spent all my life in Mannering,'' said he.

''Is that the name of the village you're going to?''

''That's it. The other side of Stratford. I'll soon be there.''

''We'll be delighted to take you there,'' said Jim. ''One place as good as another to us.''

And the old chap relaxed on the cushions and continued his endless blind staring out at the winter fields and drab little villages.

Through Stratford, he sat up and twisted this way and that, eagerly scanning the streets, stores. But when we stopped for a red light, he sat back and sank his head on his breast, as if to prevent the people crossing from seeing him in the car.

"Mmm, mmmm," said I, this time giving Jim a pinch and a sly nod in the mirror.

Back To the Old Village

Mannering, which, of course, is not its true name, nor anything like it, is a few miles beyond Stratford, and neither will I say northwest or southwest. But in a few minutes we came to the village of Mannering, just a wide place on a second-class highway, with painted cottages and old and somewhat faded red brick and yellow brick mansions, and a street of shops and cottages and two banks and one motion picture theatre.

"Which house?" asked Jim, as we started into the village asphalt.

"Just drop me anywhere," said the old chap, his voice husky.

"Not at all, not at all," cried Jim, heartily. "We'll set you down right by your door."

"Right through," said the old chap in a low voice, and turning, I saw he was almost crouched down in the back, yet stealing eager looks over the rim of the windows at the passing scene. It was growing dusk. Snow had begun. The houses seemed cuddled down, and soft lights were glowing in a few of the windows.

After we passed through the store section, the old chap sat up and leaned forward to watch ahead.

"On the left," he said, clearing his throat. "A white house. Second past this church."

But second past the church, when Jim slowed down, there was no white house. There was a brown house. A two-storey frame house, painted brown. And about it, every sign of neglect. The lawn all high-grown with weeds. It was dark. A pane of glass was broken in one of the downstairs windows.

Jim and I both felt the hands grip the cushion of our seat back.

"Vacant," said Jim, cheerfully. "Well, a couple of inquiries . . ."

"No, no," gasped the old chap, "just drop me off outside the village a bit."

"Miracles, miracles," I said casually.

Jim turned the car around on gravel. He drove slowly back to the store section, where the lights were bright and colored bulbs were festooned from store to store. In front of a little restaurant and candy store he stopped.

"Come in," he said firmly. "And we'll have a cup of coffee and a bite to eat."

The old man, bending his joints, got off the cushions and slowly stepped out of the car.

I got out and Jim and I started to escort the old fellow into the candy store. His head was bent. His hands, as they fumbled with his gray muffler, were shaking.

A man standing in the doorway next to the candy shop, festooned with boots and shoes and goloshes, suddenly stepped forward.

"Ed," he cried at our old man. "Ed."

The old man straightened and stared with his curiously bleak eyes at the stranger.

"You're Ed Stout," accused the stranger, his eyes bulging, his mouth wide in a wild grin.

Clamour And Bedlam

"Hey," roared the stranger to the wise world, to the street of Mannering, to the men and women and boys and girls busy coming and going along the street now sparkling with new falling snow. "Hey, here's Ed Stout!"

And, as if a thunderclap had sounded, as if we had driven our fist into a hornets' nest, as if we had set fire to Mannering, there was such a clamor and bedlam. "Ed Stout, Ed Stout," they shouted and squealed and yelled and men in coon coats and men in smooth coats shouldered us aside to touch Ed Stout and women, yammering, pushed sideways past us to sieze Ed Stout's hands, and children pushed and shoved and stared at Ed Stout, and from stores people came running, wiping their hands on white aprons, and above the throb, the first stranger stood roaring for somebody to run and tell the Stout boys, any of them, any one will do, that Ed Stout is home. And in less than two minutes a bell was ringing in a church or a fire hall, and cats came rushing and slithering down the street; and farmers driving teams; and the crowd grew and grew and the big stranger led Ed Stout inside the shoe store, and up and down around the store front, the mob, with faces gleaming and eyes shining and mouths jabbering "Ed Stout, Ed Stout is home, Ed Stout, Ed Stout."

"Miracle," said Jim, pulling me out to lean against our car.

"What the heck is it?" I asked.

"I don't know," said Jim, "But anyway, Ed Stout is home."

And while the mob was at its height, and two handsome men

in their forties arrived in a big black car and thrust their way into the store with everybody making way for them when they saw who they were, the tall stranger who had first seen Ed Stout came through the mob and beckoned to us.

"Come in, gentlemen," he cried.

"But what is it?" we asked.

"It's Ed Stout," said he, "home!"

"But what's the excitement?"

"Ed Stout," said the stranger, "greatest man this country ever grew. The greatest sport, the greatest friend any man ever had, and the greatest soldier. He came home from the war. He quarrelled with his young sons, who were too young to go to war at that time. You know the age?"

"Yes, yes."

"He quarrelled with his family and disappeared," said the stranger, his face like a high priest's. "And they and we and everybody all over this country have been looking for him for twenty years!"

"We're glad we picked him up," I confessed. "I guess we ought to go in and shake hands with him before we go."

"The boys took him home out the back way," said the stranger. "But I was to bring you a message from them to come up right now and have dinner with them at the Big House."

"Big House?"

"The Stout boys' house; we call it the Big House," explained the stranger.

So we went.

But Jim says this part is sacred.

The following stories originally appeared in the Star Weekly *on these dates:*

SOUVENIR – October 10, 1936

DOWN THE CHIMBLEY – December 19, 1936

YELLOW SALLY – March 13, 1937

SALES RESISTANCE – April 24, 1937

SAGA OF LOST LAKE – August 21, 1937

THE EVENING'S FISHING – July 3, 1937

"I couldn't walk around without pants even in France. So Jimmie paid a farmer to drive us into Arras in his high cart ..."

Souvenir

"**M**ORE than anything," said Jimmie Frise, "I want to revisit the actual places I was in during the war."

"Mount St. Eloi," I suggested. "Berthonval Farm."

"I'd like to stand," said Jim, "In broad daylight, in the sun, on the very spot I was wounded, up the side of Vimy Ridge. It was sleeting the night I was hit. Sleeting and I was leading two mules. We had just delivered our pack mule loads of shells to the battery, down behind the railway embankment at Petit Vimy. I was coming out, leading the mules. We were scrambling and stumbling up the muddy ridge. A path. It was sleeting. It was black as hell. Through the night, shells moaned and crashed. But I was busy."

"Mules make you busy," I agreed.

"When all of a sudden," said Jim, "there was a lovely round rainbow. A rainbow consisting of complete rings of a thousand rainbows. A million rainbows. And a vast silence and stillness and emptiness. I was floating. I was cut loose, adrift, from all this earth and its ugly, crashing cares, its long wailing sounds, its meance, its darkness, its cold, stinging sleet."

"It's mules," I helped.

"And when I woke up, it was a hospital in a big tent," said Jim. "I have forgotten even the mules' names."

"Was there no pain?" I asked.

"Just rainbows," said Jim. "No bang. No hurt. No nothing. Just concentric rainbows, millions of them, all one inside the other."

"I was never wounded," I said sadly.

"I want to stand," said Jim, "right on that spot in daylight, in sunlight, and look out across the plain of Vimy, all green and spattered with little ten-house villages. The birds singing. The wheat growing. It will wipe away a lot of the shabby tatters of memory. I can love France, if I see that the place I remember does not exist. Perhaps never did exist."

"Oh, it existed," I assured him. "But from what we saw of it on the pilgrimage, there isn't much we can recognize."

"There were too many of us," said Jim. "Just the two of us on a sentimental pilgrimage of remembrance. We can poke around and take our time. We'll dig up something."

So we left Paris in the early morning, Paris with its immensity and sense of newness, yet built, like the rings of a tree's growth, upon layers and layers of things dreadfully old. Left Paris in one of those ferocious French trains that go shrieking through the lovely country with a whistle like a peanut cart. Lovely trains that make ours seem like some kind of an old wagon. And we went through Albert and saw the new Virgin, standing erect once more, her Babe held high above her head. Saw little scabby old villages like the ones we knew in the war. Then got into the war zone and saw the lovely new shining villages, so utterly unlike the ones we remembered. The new villages, built with reparations money. Better villages than any Frenchman has seen since the Romans.

Looking in Vain

And Jimmie excitedly pointed out what he said were gun pits and emplacements along the sides of sunken roads near Albert, though they looked to my infantry eye like something the rain had washed out. And as we came towards Arras, I pointed out Telegraph Hill to Jimmie, though he said it looked like a nice bit of farming country to him. And we arrived in Arras, where English-speaking taxi drivers spotted us for pilgrims and offered to drive us all around the district for 300 francs.

But we wanted to stroll in Arras, which we did. Last time we saw it, it was an earthquake ruin. A vast gray shambles. Crudely, savagely wrecked. We lived in the cellars of Arras.

We had expected Arras to be restored. We expected a sleepy old country town, with a rebuilt cathedral all wrong, and junky little rebuilt modern shops and cottages. We found ourselves strolling in a city centuries old, with its massive stone buildings, antiquely carved; its faded old paint on sign and timber; cobbled streets, squares, shops with modern chromium-plated fronts, full of lingerie three hours from Paris; cream-colored taxis, swank gendarmes, wicker street cafes, speed, color, age, charm.

"How did they do it?" I gasped.

"With war reparations money," said Jim, "and the clever use of all the old stone that wasn't shelled to dust."

"But you would think it was centuries old," I said.

"It is nearly twenty years old," said Jim, "and that gives buildings long enough to get the shine off them. And the French are smart enough to know that they haven't got the taste in building their ancestors had."

From Arras we walked out the Lens road, a modern asphalt highway. Looked in vain for a single sign of Madagascar Dump or the Ecurie or Etrun we had known. Bright, merry, brick villages full of children and peace and gardens.

Saw the twin ruined steeple of Mount St. Eloi shining whitely in the distance. Came to Neuville St. Vaast. Neuville St. Vaast, we used to doubt had ever been a village. We thought it had been a Roman ruin for two thousand years before the war.

But here before our eyes was a fine village of pretty cottages, brick and stone, cafes, butcher shops.

"They shouldn't call it Neuville St. Vaast," said Jimmie, indignantly. "They ought to give new names to these places."

"To think," I said, "we came two thousand miles over here and did a big job. Smashed things up. Gave everybody a lesson. Made our mark in the world. And now look at it. You'd never know we had been here."

We chatted our way through the pretty village, asking everyone if they knew where there might be some old shell holes or bits of trench or a gun pit, maybe, where a couple of old soldiers might sit and rest. But nobody knew. They smiled in the friendliest way, but the only trenches they knew of were some the Canadians had preserved with concrete a few miles north. Somewhere, out that way. No. They had never been there to see them. Trenches did not interest them. A gang of little boys followed us, as if we might tell war stories to them. We found an elderly woman, with raven hair, who spoke a slow deep English.

"Do you know," I asked, "where the Pylones Trench used to be? Somewhere just north of about here?"

"I could not know," she said.

"You are a stranger here?" I inquired.

"I am born here. I have live here all my life. Except the war."

"The Pylones Trench," I said. "Everybody knew it. A great deep trench."

"You lived here in the war," smiled the dark lady. "You will know."

"It was revetted," I said. "It had cement reinforcing. It was very strong. It would last."

"With a great deal of trouble," said the dark lady, "we cleaned this all up; trouble and not a little love of a place as we can say in the French."

"Out that way," I said, "towards Thelus, out there where the Lens Road goes down, by the cable house and the ecole commune, would there be old trenches?"

"Farms, very excellent," said the dark lady. "And some plantations of little fir trees by the government of Canada to whom we have given a piece of ground for their so beautiful monument. It is we who should erect the monument to you for your friendship that made you to die."

So we went east and north out of Neuville St. Vaast and talked to a gendarme on a bicycle, who could tell us only that there might be some ruins of trench and dugout amidst the little fir trees that clothe the scene of the Canadian tempest up Vimy Ridge. A rich wood grows where those skeleton trees used to stand ghastly summer and winter, along the crest. A deep green wood. They call it the Bois de la Folie, as we did. But now it is a bois, and a nightingale sings there in the gloaming and in the early morning.

Into that plantation of six-foot fir trees we penetrated and toiled through briars and weeds looking for some vestige, some shadow of the mark we made in our time. It was hard going. The fir trees are planted close. The spaces are lush with tall weeds and tight branches. And not until we had been looking for an hour did we suddenly observe that the worst part of our hard going was due to the uneveness of the ground.

"Why," cried Jim, "we're actually walking in shell holes. And trenches. All these billows..."

"But shell holes," I protested, "were six, eight, ten feet deep."

"Twenty years ago they were," replied Jim.

And right away we laid down our haversacks and cameras and sat outselves in the sun on this sacred earth and remembered.

"There can be no way," said Jim, "I could find the mule track down the front, where I was hit."

"There can be no way," I admitted, "that I could even find the old Canadian and German front lines. If I could locate some trace of them, I am pretty sure I could get an idea of about where we are."

But in the little jungle of merciful and enfolding fir trees, you could not see the spires of Arras or even the guiding finger of Mont St. Eloi Tower.

After a rest, we stumbled on, seeking something that could be imagined even to look like a trench. But what appeared to be a bit of trench vanished away in briar and fir and tumble and jumble. And another afternoon hour went by before Jim let out a sharp cry.

"Wire underfoot," he yelled.

And there, sure enough, was a tangle of rusted and rotten old wire coiled around Jim's leg.

"It's the front line," I shouted. "See. This zig and that zag. Front line. This is a bay I'm standing on, and you're on a traverse."

And joyously, we pushed among the bay first, tracing out bits of meandering trench, now, alas, not two feet deep, just a memory, a shadow of a trench. But trench, so help us. And thrusting farther, we came to what was undeniably the old German front. Here the wire was thicker than ever, the long barbed, cruel German wire. The wire lashed and laced and enduring that the Fritz knew how to string.

"Careful, Jim," I said. "It still tears. I've got a rip in my pant leg already."

"You're the infantry," said Jim.

We thrust through the brambles and bushes, came to deeper holes that must have been giant shell craters in their day; lost the shadowy remnant and found it again. But nowhere did I see a familiar bend, a remembered vista. We might just as well have been looking for trenches around Lake Superior.

"Whoa," called Jimmie, who was some distance behind the infantry, as was only proper.

"What have you got?" I asked.

"I'm tangled up in some wire," laughed Jim. "Hey, give us a hand."

"Well," I said, "it takes the artillery to get stuck in the holes."

"Give me a hand, will you," said Jim. "I seem to be tangled in a nest of it."

Cautiously, I thrust the brambles aside and worked my way into the depression towards Jim.

"The infantry," I was in the act of saying, "always had to come and help..."

When my foot caught and I fell roughly into the briars.

"Easy," commanded Jim.

I threw myself back into a sitting position deep in the brambles and felt something take me firmly by the leg. Pressing the weeds and briars apart, I beheld a regular Hindenburg Line of barbed wire hidden in the briars of the little hollow.

"Jim," I said, "I'm badly tangled here. Get yourself free and come give me a hand."

Jim bent down and after a few seconds got free and came to my aid. He got me under the arms and hoisted. We heard ripping. I braced myself with my other leg and heaved. I felt it quietly seized by slender and clasping arms. A faint chill ran through me. A chill of remembrance.

"Quit," I yelled.

And Jim dropped me. I sat down heavily.

"Now, my friend," I said, "thanks to your artillery tactics, I am caught fore and aft."

So Jim knelt down and reconnoitred and I rolled delicately this way and that while Jim attempted to loosen the aged and rusted but still enduring tendrils of a bygone hate. Both legs were variously and thoroughly snagged and the seat and back of my trousers were punctured and embroiled; and with every struggle to free one leg, not only did the other leg grow worse, but the wire, imprisoned by twenty years of brambles, appeared to reach eagerly for my upper regions.

"As I see it," said Jim, cautiously avoiding the wire, "you'll have to sacrifive your pants in order to extricate your main body."

"Nonsense," I said. "Let's break off the wire."

But our effort to twist the wire only enmeched me worse. And at last, with Jim again lifting me, I shed my nether garment.

"Now," I said, "reach in and rescue them."

"Not with a ten-foot pole," said Jim.

"But, good heavens, man, I can't go around without pants, not even in France," I protested.

"Rescue them yourself," said Jim, retreating to high ground well clear of the pernicious hollow.

But wherever I peered in under the brambles, sly, coiling strands of wire appeared. And pulls from various angles only ripped the flannel.

"Jim," I said, "what am I to do?"

"Walk behind me" said Jim, "and carry both our haversacks, slung long on their straps. They'll cover you some. And we'll hail the first conveyance to Arras and a gents' furnishings."

Which plan we followed to Neuville St. Vaast, avoiding the highway and going cross country; and in the village an old farmer gladly accepted ten francs to drive us, in his high cart, to Arras.

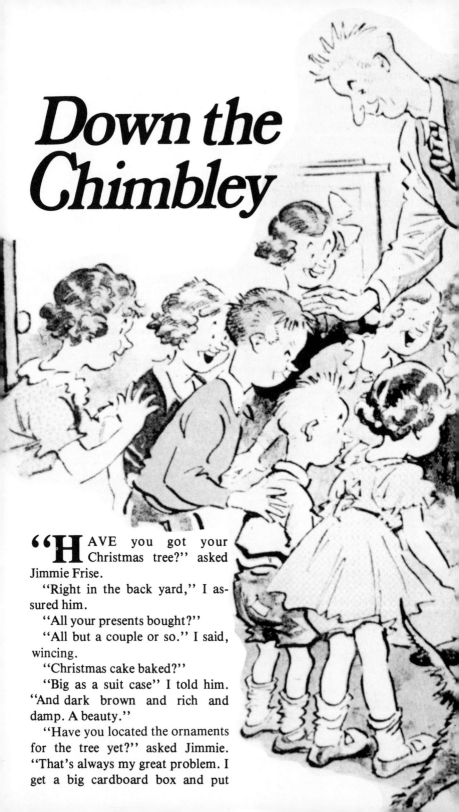

Down the Chimbley

"**H**AVE you got your Christmas tree?" asked Jimmie Frise.

"Right in the back yard," I assured him.

"All your presents bought?"

"All but a couple or so." I said, wincing.

"Christmas cake baked?"

"Big as a suit case" I told him. "And dark brown and rich and damp. A beauty."

"Have you located the ornaments for the tree yet?" asked Jimmie. "That's always my great problem. I get a big cardboard box and put

"It would certainly be a surprise to all our kids if I came pop down our chimney ..."

away all the Christmas tree ornaments and tinsel and everything for the next year. Then I hide it somewhere. And it takes me a week to find it.''

"It isn't the ornaments stick me," I said. "It's that three-legged iron thing you stand the Christmas tree in I can't find. I hunt the house from cellar to attic, and I cuss and yell around the house, and never can find it. Then I try nailing pieces of flat board on the bottom of the tree, to make it stand up, but it leans crooked. And after I have worked myself into a pale fury and all the Christmas spirit has oozed out of me, one of the boys says: 'Why don't you use that thing you had last year, that iron thing?' And he goes and gets it where it has been all the time. Hanging on the wall down cellar.''

"Well, I must say," said Jim, "I'm better prepared for Christmas than I have ever been. All my gifts bought. Turkey hanging in the back kitchen. Christmas tree lights all checked over and new colored bulbs bought, with a couple of spares in case of emergency.''

"There's certainly little surprise left to Christmas," I declared. "You can feel Christmas coming weeks away. It builds and builds,until a week before Christmas, you might almost say it is Christmas. I think we lose some of the joy of Christmas by that build up.''

"It didn't use to be that way," agreed Jimmie, "when we were young. It was more secret. There was always a sense of tremendous surprise about Christmas morning. You knew Christmas was coming, but there were no signs of it. You went to bed Christmas Eve with a feeling of immense anticipation. Except for a certain excitement in your elders, however, there was no sign. No decorations. No parcels half hidden on shelves or under beds. Not even a holly wreath in the door.''

"I remember," I said.

"Then Christmas morning," cried Jim. "And you wake to find, hanging to the knobs of your bed, huge stockings bulging and bursting with oranges, white and pink cream candies and nuts, and a toy sticking tremendously out of the top of the whole thing.''

"A jumping jack," I recollected, "on a stick "

"Then you were called triumphantly downstairs," went on Jim, "and before you got half way down the stairs, you could smell the tree, and there were loops of evergreen and holly festooned around the hall chandeliers, and as you ran, almost weak with expectation, down to the bottom, there burst on you the parlor, transformed beyond belief. Holly and evergreens and bright paper everywhere, a tree all spangled and glittering, the mantel, ordinarily so prim and severe, with its pallid marble clock, and its one or two Dresden china figures, all rowdy and gay with holly and packages of dolls propped up and colored paper horns..."

Aren't Surprised Any More

"I remember that mantel," I declared. "What a cold, intimidating thing the parlor mantel was, now that you remind me. Cold, formal, forbidding. It chilled our childish lives. It repressed us, like a physical admonition. It stood there, staring coldly at us as we rushed through the house..."

"On the mantel," interrupted Jimmie, "there would be not only propped up dolls and colored paper horns, but red and white candy canes. And tall-stemmed cut glass candy dishes, glittering beautifully, that never came out of their hiding until Christmas."

"Oh, it was a surprise," I admitted fondly.

"It was better than Christmas is now," said Jim.

"I'm sorry," I confessed, "for my kids. No surprise any more. Just a great big build up, and when the reality dawns, it is never up to expectations."

"I believe you're right," admitted Jim.

"It's hopeless," I explained, "to try to do it the old-fashioned way, because, even if in our homes we tried to keep Christmas secret, the stores and the streets and the radio and the newspaper would give it away."

"Surely there's some way," said Jim, "we could introduce a little element of surprise into Christmas for our kids. I mean, after all, we owe our children something. We have no right to let a lovely old thing die, a thing like the old-fashioned Christmas."

"We could invite a big party," I suggested. "It seems to me there were always about twenty-five people sat down to Christmas dinner when I was a child. Now, there's just the family. And maybe a couple of in-laws."

"Cousins and aunts", said Jim, "aren't as popular as they used to be, I guess. It seems as if the past twenty-five years development in transportation, like the highways and motor cars and so forth, didn't bring families closer together but scattered them farther apart."

"I don't suppose a big family party for Christmas would surprise the kids," I mused. "They'd only be bored."

"Don't pull that stuff about the modern cnild," warned Jim. "It isn't our kids' fault if they aren't surprised any more at anything."

"The greatest surprise I ever got," I told Jim, "was when I was about nine years old. I had just nicely got over believing in Santa Claus. We were to my grandma's for Christmas that year, and my Uncle Tom got dressed up as Santa Claus. The house was full of aunts and uncles and cousins, a great big family gathering. Well, sir, when we came down, all breathless, to the big living room, there was the Christmas tree with nary a gift on it, and no gifts anywhere, on the mantel or anywhere else. And all our aunts and uncles were nearly crying with disappointment for us. What a scene! In the early morning, with candles lighted, and a kind of eerie light. And everybody standing around in dismay and weeping."

"What a trick," said Jim.

Never Sure of Anything Since

"All of a sudden," I told, "the door bell rang, and one of my uncles ran to the door, but it was only a telegram. A telegram from Santa Claus saying he had been delayed by the storm, but telling us to wait he would be along any minute. And hardly had we read this when we heard a wild sound of sleigh bells, and there, out the window, when we rushed, was a great red cutter, with four lovely horses in it, and out of it jumped Santa Claus, in the dawn, and came running up the front walk with a huge bag on his back."

"Quite a shock", said Jim, "for anybody not believing in Santa Claus."

"It was the first time," I assured him, "I lost my assurance. I have never been sure of anything since. There was no doubt about it. There was Santa Claus, in the flesh. He burst in the front door and started unloading that vast bundle, and he ran back to his sleigh and got more. Some of the older kids said the horses and cutter looked mighty like Doyle's livery, but Santa Claus merely said he had rented it, since his reindeer were stuck in a drift. Between opening our gifts and looking at Santa Claus, we had no time to think about it. It cost me two bloody noses before I failed to believe in Santa Claus again."

"I wish," said Jim, wistfully, " we could give Santa Claus back to our kids."

"Why not?" I demanded. "I'm the right size to make a nice Santa Claus."

"They'd know you, in a second," said Jim.

"I could arrive in some mysterious way," I suggested.

"Where could you get a red cutter and four prancing horses now?" asked Jim sadly.

"I could doll my car up with red and white ribbon," I offered.

"Cheap," said Jim. "No imagination. No surprise."

"It certainly would be a surprise to all our kids," I laughed, "if I could come pop down a chimney. But there are no chimneys any more."

"There are though!" cried Jim excitedly. "There's a chimney running up from my den. My den was built on after the rest of the house was built. There's a huge fireplace in it I have never used, and a great big chimney."

"Jimmie," I said.

"Yes, sir," said Jim, "several summers ago, an owl or something got into the chimney and I remember looking up to see. It's a chimney almost two feet square. That's big enough."

"Jim," I said, "we could bring all the children over to your house and have Christmas there. And me coming down the chimney — oh boy!"

"Come over and see it," exclaimed Jim. "The first night the kids are out to the movies, I'll call you."

Old-Fashioned Fireplace

So we had the house to ourselves last night and went into conference. Jim's den is one of those dens with guns on the wall and sewing machines in the corners. A fine business-like desk, with a lot of toys piled all over it. A real family man's den.

But the fireplace. A wide, old-fashioned fireplace for burning sawlogs in, if there were any sawlogs. No soot stained its handsome white stone.

"Except for a little dust and plaster," said Jim, "you can come down that chimney in your Santa Claus suit as clean as a whistle."

"Now," I said, "for figuring out the ways and means."

With a flashlight, we peered up the huge chimney. It was certainly an old-fashioned one. It was wide and square, and you could see stars through the top of it.

"We could rig a strong pole across the top," said Jim,"and you could then lower yourself, with a rope."

"Better still, " I said, "if the walls are close enough, I could let myself down by squeezing my elbows against the sides and let myself down a little at a time."

"Let's go to the attic," said Jim. "There's a window lets out on the roof there. We can actually look it over from the top."

Out a good wide gable, we were able to crawl to the chimney. With our flashlight, we studied down the bricky and mortar-crusted chasm. It was no more than twenty-five feet. Perhaps

78

not that.

"I imagine," I said, "I could let myself down, inch by inch, without a rope. That mortar sticking out between each row of bricks will help me grip with my knees and elbows."

"See if you fit," said Jim.

"You mean now?" I asked.

"Sure," said Jim. "Get in and see if it fits you. If it doesn't, we can rig up a pole across here and you can lower yourself with the rope."

Carefully I threw a leg over the chimney and hoisted myself on to it. Longitudinally, I discovered I was much too slim. I would shoot down the chimney the way a pea goes out of a pea shooter. But by drawing up my knees and elbows, I found I was more than a snug fit.

"It fits fine," I said.

"Lower yourself a couple of inches." said Jim.

I hinched myself a few inches down. The mortar squeezed out between the bricks made a good braking surface.

"It's easy, Jim," I assured him. "I can come down this way, dragging my bags behind me."

"Will I give you a hand up?" said Jim.

"Now that I'm down this far," I said, "I might as well go all the way. I'll get a little dusty, that's all."

"Go ahead," said Jim enthusiastically. "I'll run down and meet you at the fireplace."

I started lowering myself. Holding with my elbows, I would lower with my knees. Then hold with my knees and lower my elbows. Like an inch worm, or like a South Sea Island and coconut hunter, I lowered myself a few inches at a time.

A Santa Claus Rehearsal

"Boy," shouted Jim boomingly up the fireplace, "how's it coming?"

"Famous," I said.

But at that moment, I struck a lot of loose or crumbly mortar which broke off instead of acting as a brake, and I slipped sharply about a foot down.

"Get a pillow, Jim," I shouted. "Get something. I'm slipping."

I slipped another violent jolt. I felt smooth bricks around me.

"Jim," I said, "how far up am I?"

"About ten feet," said Jim, below.

"I'm stuck?" I informed him.

"How stuck?" demanded Jim indignantly.

"Stuck by my middle," I said. "The chimney must get narrow here. It's wide enough one way and not wide enough the other."

"Wiggle," commanded Jim.

I wiggled. I held my breath. I contracted myself. But there was no give. I was snugly wedged.

"Jim," I said sharply, "bring a rope. Come up and get me out of this before I settle. If I get stuck here you'll have to tear the house down."

In a moment, I heard Jim's voice from above, calling down the chimney.

"Push up with your knees," he called. "One you get loose, you can hoist yourself up the same way you let yourself down."

"What do you think I've been doing the past few minutes?" I said angrily. "The more I struggle the tighter I set. Drop me a rope. Quick."

"Wait a minute," said Jim. "I'll lower myself down and you can grab hold of my foot. Work yourself loose, holding it, and then worm yourself back up the way you got down."

"Hurry," I said.

Jim, holding to the chimney top, could not quite reach my upraised hands with his feet. So he lowered himself very carefully. I felt a shower of mortar coming raining down.

"Careful," I yelled.

But it was too late. I heard Jim grunt. I felt his boots come down smartly on to my upraised hands, then on to my shoulders and head.

"Ugh," he said, struggling.

"Now," said I, "Mr. Santa Claus, now you've done it."

He struggled and panted, but I knew he was only wedging himself tighter and coming momentarily closer down on top of me.

"How soon," I asked, "do you expect the children home?"

"After the show," said Jim, in muffled tones.

"Try yelling," I shouted.

"Nobody would believe it if they did hear it," yelled back Jimmie.

"What will we do?" I begged.

"Sit tight," said Jim, "until the kids get home. Then they can lower a rope."

Which we did.

And did we ever surprise those kids?

Yellow Sally

"**A**T last," said Jimmie Frise, "at long last, I am about to buy a new car."

"Jim," I congratulated him, "it's about time. What make are you choosing?"

"When I say a new car," stated Jim, "I do not mean a new car in the full meaning of the word. It will be a used car."

"Oh, not another second-hand car," I protested.

"A used car," repeated Jim. "There

"Why, she looks new," cried Jim, walking around the beauty. "Oh, I had her washed up," admitted Mr. Gitch frankly.

ought to be a better word than used car. Matured car. Ripe car. Car tuned in or broken in.''

"Broken in," I assured him, "is the word. Will you never learn to profit by other people's mistakes?"

"I do profit by other people's mistakes," said Jimmie, "Profit very neatly, too. And the only mistake they make is turning in a car just when it is getting prime."

"You've never yet bought a new car," I accused him. "In eighteen years you have never had anything but used cars."

"I would just as soon," declared Jim, "pick a green banana off the tree and eat it as buy a new car. I like my cars to be run in and matured before I get them. Let somebody else pay for a lot of shine and stiff engine. Let somebody else have the grief of seeing dents and scratches come on that investment. Let somebody else have the doubtful pleasure of driving it during its infancy at twenty-five miles an hour for the next 500 miles."

"If you have never had the pleasure of driving a beautiful smooth new car, Jim," I informed him, "you are hardly in a position to judge that pleasure".

"Let somebody else," continued Jimmie, "have the fun of paying for all the adjustments and replacements that have to be made on a car before it is right."

"New cars," I advised, "are guaranteed for 90 days."

"Yes," said Jim, "and for the first 80 days you own a new car, you are conscious of it every time you are in it. You take special care of it. Give it oil. Treat it with consideration. There is blame little likely to happen the works of a new car in the first 90 days. But in 180 days, you lose that first fine rapture and begin to put the car really to work. You have lost your silly pride in it. You step on it. You neglect its oil and grease a little. Whatever defects there were in it come to the surface. And our proud first owner has to pay for those corrections."

"You make me feel," I said, "as if I had been a fool for fifteen years."

"There always have to be fools," said Jim kindly. "But I have a line on a car, a swell sport model Allnox Eight."

"What year?" I asked.

"A 1930," said Jim. "But it has belonged to a man who has spent most of his time abroad and down in Florida. A rich guy, apparently. And it has spent most of its life in a garage. It has only gone 16,000 miles."

"The price?" I asked.

"Prepare yourself," said Jim triumphantly. "Get set. Take hold of something for support. Only $400."

"There must be something wrong with it," I said. "A new Allnox Eight is $2,200."

With a Weasel Smile

"I telephoned this guy last night," said Jim excitedly. "It's a private deal. No dealers, he said. He's going on another trip abroad and he says he sees no reason for keeping this car laid up in his garage all the time. But he realizes it is a 1930 model and he is willing to let it go at a nominal figure, despite its wonderful condition."

"What color is it?" I asked.

"Daffodil yellow," cried Jimmie. "And he says it looks as if it had just come from the factory."

"Are you going to see it?" I inquired.

"Am I going to see it?" shouted Jim. "Have I got the $400 in my mitt? Have I an appointment to see it at noon to-day?"

"How about...?" I began.

"Certainly," said Jim. "I expect you to come with me."

The neighborhood to which we drove to inspect the Allnox Eight was hardly the type of district a rich man would choose to live in. As a matter of fact, we were doubtful if we had the right house when we rang the bell because there were "roomer" signs in the windows. But this was all explained by Mr. Gitch when the landlady called him to the door.

Mr. Gitch was a small lean man who looked as if he were wearing somebody else's clothes. He had a smooth tapered face that made him look like either a fox or a greyhound, and his eyes had that slitty, greyhound appearance of being able to see around to the back. Still, lots of men look rather funny by the time they are rich. You can't get rich for nothing, I always say.

"Gentlemen," said Mr. Gitch, softly, coming out on the porch, "I have the car around at the back. You will pardon my diggings here, but as I explained to you, I am seldom in Toronto and whenever I am, I stay with this dear old soul who was a chum of my dear mother."

He led us around the narrow side entrance and through a yard full of junk and boxes, to a lane. All the way through, he continued to explain in his soft, tender voice.

"After stopping at such places as the Ritz in London," he smiled, "and the Ambassadoria in Rio and the Hotel London in Shanghai, you would imagine I would find it a little irksome to stop in a neighborhood like this."

He smiled up at us from under his forehead and shook his hand delicately at the junk around. It seemed to me I had seen a weasel smile at me like that in the instant it had appeared in the grass along a country fence.

"But this dear old body," he chuckled, "would be simply heart broken if she heard I was in Toronto and had not stayed with her."

He pushed through a hole in the back fence where a plank was off and there, there, stood the Allnox Eight.

Daffodil yellow, sure enough; and gleaming, flatly indeed, as if she had come straight from the factory. Not a dent or a scratch marred her satiny glowing surface.

"Why, she looks new," cried Jim, walking around the beauty.

"Oh, I had her washed up," admitted Mr. Gitch, frankly.

Inside, her upholstery was covered with dust covers of of a snappy color and design, securely fastened down with tapes. It seemed to me that here and there, faint signs of age showed on her, such as the nickel of the lamps and felt around the windows. I wordlessly placed my fingers on these slight omens, but Jimmie ignored my hints and walked around the car with increasing excitement.

Nature is Completely Honest

Mr. Gitch followed him with a curious softness of foot and voice that made me think of a cat.

"Hop in," said Mr; Gitch. "We'll take a spin."

He drove. We rolled smoothly along the lane and into the streets full of bakers' wagons and under-school-age children. Mr. Gitch raced the engine to show its power, since, obviously we could not let her out in these narrow streets.

"Listen to that", cried Jim. "Has she ever got power?"

"At 16,000 miles," said Mr. Gitch, "if these American cars are on a par with American cars such as I am familiar with, I should say she was just nicely run in."

He steered her around the block and back into the lane, where we dismounted.

"How about it?" asked Mr. Gitch, and while I could not be sure, it seemed to me I saw his hands clutching and unclutching the way a hawk's talons do.

"It's a deal," said Jim. "Can you drive her downtown to my office? We'll drive down there and meet you and close the deal.''

"That," said Mr. Gitch "would suit me perfectly.''

"Meet me in half an hour then," said Jim, "right in front of the office. I'll be waiting there.''

We hastened out to my car and as I slammed the door, I cried, "Jim, there's something phoney about this whole thing. Call it off. Have the car examined by a mechanic.''

"What's that?" demanded Jim, coming out of his trance.

"Something phoney," I repeated. "I don't like the man.''

"It's the car we are buying," retorted Jim. "Is there anything wrong with the car?''

"Nature," I declared, "is pretty honest in putting on the outside of all her packages a description of the contents. A crow is black and evil looking. A fox is sly and slinky. A deer is graceful and timid and shy-looking. If a man looks like a pig, you are generally pretty safe in assuming that he is a pig. If a man looks like a fox, he is generally sly. If he...''

"What are you giving us?" snorted Jim.

"It's a fact," I assured him. "Nature is completely honest. She rarely fakes the outside of a bad package. Men are different. They can fake up the outside to look like a million dollars. That man reminded me of a fox, a weasel and a hawk. I don't like him.''

"Listen," said Jim, "if we went around buying stuff only from the people we liked the look of, were would we be at?''

"We would be a lot better off," I stated.

"I guess," smiled Jim, "you're just a little jealous. As a new car buyer, you are just a little ribbed on seeing what kind of deals can be made if you look around. Oh, boy, can you see me sailing around in that yellow baby? That's a sportsman's car. Can you see me going to the races in it? Or out in the country, on a fishing trip?''

"Jim," I said, "it's phoney. It looks all right, it seemed to run all right. But that man is a weasel.''

"Haw, haw," laughed Jim.

So we came to the office and parked my car and went and stood in front of the building to await Mr. Gitch. As we stood there waiting, our old friend Constable McGonigle came sauntering along and stopped to have a chat with us. He belongs to the anglers' association and is one of the most distinguished pike fishermen in the country despite his enormous size. Most good anglers are on the small side, but Constable McGonigle is a notable exception. We chatted merrily about the fast approaching season, Jimmie keeping a weather eye open for Mr. Gitch and Constable McGonigle keeping a weather eye open for the sergeant; and suddenly Jimmie cried:

"Here he comes."

Waiting For Delivery

Mr. Gitch in the magnificent yellow car was slowing down to come in to the open space where we were standing.

But suddenly he seemed to change his mind. He swung the wheel and stepped on the gas and with a roar of the engine leaped away and all we could see was the great yellow car vanishing along the street swaying in the traffic.

"What the dickens," said Jim.

"What was all that?" asked Constable McGonigle .

So we explained to Constable McGonigle about the impending purchase and arranged to take him along with us on the first fishing trip in the new car which, in honor of the trout fly of that name, we agreed to call Yellow Sally. And he sauntered on, leaving Jimmie and me to wait for Mr. Gitch to come back around the block.

"Maybe," said Jim, "he was just showing us how it handles."

"Maybe," I suggested, "he thought this space wasn't big enough for him to park."

We waited five minutes, ten minutes; no Mr. Gitch. We walked right around the block and met Constable McGonigle again but he said he had noticed no yellow car.

At the end of an hour, we decided to go back to Mr. Gitch's and see what had happened. A sad little old lady opened the door and we asked for Mr. Gitch."

"Mr. Who?" said she.

"Mr. Gitch," we explained, "the gentleman we called for this morning, about a big yellow car he was selling."

"Oh, him," said the landlady. "He only rented the room for an hour this morning, I never saw him before."

"Ah," said Jim.

"But," said the lady, "maybe you could get him at a garage three streets over. I forget the name, but they have a big garage three streets over. I noticed that big yellow car backing out of it only yesterday, the same one he had in the lane this morning."

Hastily Jim and I drove along to the garage which we found without trouble and we asked for the boss.

"A big yellow car?" he said. "Sure, we did the paint job on it just this week.

"Paint job," said Jim.

"One of the best paint jobs we ever did," said the boss. "It set him back $70. But he insisted. We did a swell paint job and we trimmed up all the nickel and we sewed down a new set of dust covers on the seats and you wouldn't know it from a new car hardly. That is, by the looks."

"Was it in pretty good shape?" asked Jim.

"Pretty good shape?" asked the boss. "It was the worst old wreck I ever had in this place. He got it for $50 and he spent $70 on it. Can you imagine that?"

"Heh, heh," laughed Jimmie.

"But he said in his business - he's a salesman," explained the garage boss, "he says appearances are everything."

"Well, if he turns up," said Jim, "tell him a couple of people were looking for him."

"I doubt if he'll be back," said the boss. "He told me he was heading for California."

So we drove back down town, and on the way, we stopped and bought a nice box of cigars for Constable McGonigle.

And Jim says it is always best to take a mechanic along with you when you got to look at a used car.

And before Mr. McDucky's speechless gaze ... Jim put the clock through its marvellous paces.

Sales Resistance

"**W**E," said Jimmie Frise, "should have been salesmen."

"Heaven forbid," I stated.

"Selling is the game," said Jimmie. "That's where the big money lies."

"All a salesman needs," I declared, "is good legs."

"A lot you know about it," laughed Jim. "Why, I know a salesman in the refrigerator business - he sells big hotels and packing houses - who made $7,000 yesterday."

"Yesterday?" I expostulated.

"Yesterday," said Jim. "In one day, he made $7,000."

"It doesn't seem right," I protested. "Nobody should be allowed to make $7,000 in one day. It doesn't stand to reason."

"Well, said Jim, " he gets ten per cent commission. And he sold $70,000 worth of refrigerating equipment to a chain of packing houses. So there."

"It still sounds criminal," I protested. "A guy making $7,000 in one day. No wonder there is unrest in the world."

"Would you object," asked Jimmie, "to a man making $7,000 a year?"

"Ah, no," I admitted, "not in a year. That's more sensible."

"Well, in this case," said Jim, "my friend worked a whole year to get this order. So you might say, while he actually put over the deal yesterday, it was the result of a year's hard and anxious labor."

"Now it makes sense," I agreed. "I can just see the poor devil. Calling day after day, week after week, on these pork packers. Having to drive up, every little while, to the packing house district, into that odor, and sit around half smothered in it, waiting for the big executives to see him. I can picture the slow agony of the weeks and months as they drag by, and this poor salesman, a big shot in his own line, but still just a palooka outside the pork packer's door, hoping and praying. Having to jump up delightedly and beam all over every time the old pig sticker condescended to see him, until gradually he gets to hate the very sight of the cow chopper. I guess he earned his $7,000 all right."

"I still think selling is the great game," stated Jimmie.

"You can have it," I agreed.

"As a matter of fact," said Jim, "I've been reading a very interesting book on salesmanship."

"At your age?" I cried.

"There are two kinds of selling," explained Jim. "There is ordinary selling, like in stores and shops, where there is very little sales resistance on the part of the public. The public just comes in willingly to buy. You stand in your store and sell. Some of the drug stores have got pretty scientific at even this kind of selling. For instance, when you go in for a bottle of cough mixture, they try to sell you a mustard plaster. Or if you ask for razor blades, they flash before your eyes a swift succession of shaving soap, shaving brushes, face lotion, and that sort of thing."

"I know it well," I assured him. "Barbers invented that method."

The Life Germ of Business

"The other kind of selling," said Jim, "is where the science and art of selling comes in. In this case, the salesman goes to the customer, instead of the customer going to the store. All the major selling in the world is handled in this way. The big corporations have purchasing agents who sit in their offices interviewing an endless procession of salesmen who call upon them. But over and above the purchasing agent kind of selling, there is a super salesmanship."

"Golf links salesmanship?" I guessed.

"Yes," said Jim, "it's the supreme form of selling. And men who succeed in it are artists. It includes salesmen of all kinds, from door to door men selling screen door stoppers to the giants of salesmanship who sell railroads or banks or pulp and paper mills to unsuspecting customers."

"I prefer," I confessed, "to just sit down and write. And you should be happy, just to draw cartoons. Why read books on salesmanship at this time of year? And why talk about them to your friends? There are some hobbies that are not mutual, and salesmanship is one of them."

"Listen," said Jim, intensely, "we are salesmen. What is writing a story but salesmanship? What is drawing a cartoon but selling an idea or a smile? I tell you we are fools to stay in this finger-twiddling business. We have been merely putting in an apprenticeship at learning what people like. Now let us go forth and cash in on what we have learned."

"Jim," I warned, "haven't you learned long ago not to tamper with other lines of business? Haven't we got into jam after jam, from trying to pick up a little loose change in other ways?"

"It's a heck of a life," muttered Jim, "trying to make people laugh."

Marvellous Possibilities

"What would you sell?" I asked him.

"A good salesman," said Jim, "can sell anything. But a relative of mine is sales manager of an electric clock outfit. They make a new clock that is the most wonderful thing I ever saw. It looks like an ordinary clock but it runs silently, you just plug it into the wall like a light."

"I've seen them," I said.

"Not this one, you haven't," said Jimmie. "It has a little panel on the back with various gadgets. You can set it to ring an alarm at various times. For instance, you want to get up at 7.30 a.m., and you don't want to forget to call the bank at 10 and the vacuum cleaner people at noon and remind the music teacher that Greg won't be to his lesson to-day at three and so forth. That clock rings a bell at those various times as a reminder.''

"Not a bad gadget," I confessed.

"Ah, but listen," said Jim, it will also ring a bell automatically when it starts to rain. It will function as a burglar alarm by simply attaching a wire to a small device on the doors and windows. And it can be set to turn off all the lights in the house at a certain hour so that you can go to bed at night without worrying about the downstairs or the cellar lights.''

"Jimmie," I cried.

"It's the most wonderful thing, this clock," said Jim. "It will sell like hot cakes, all over a certain section of this city. They figure there are 28,000 Toronto homes that will want it.''

"Of course they will," I agreed.

"It sells for only $15," said Jim, "with various de luxe models at $25, $50 and $75. And the salesman gets fifty per cent.''

"Fifty per cent?" I gasped.

"I figure," said Jim, "a man could sell say ten of them a day.''

"A hundred a day, you mean," I assured him.

"Say twenty a day," said Jim. "And figure only on the standard model, at $15. There would be twenty times $7.50, which is $160 a day straight commission to the salesman.''

"Great scott, Jimmie,". I cried, "how many salesman has he got yet?''

"He wanted me to take over a few," said Jim, "and to sell to my friends.''

"Why, Jimmie!" I shouted, leaping up.

And the ways and means committee went into session right there. Selling to acquaintances and friends, we agreed, was the coward's path. Secondly, we agreed to work together, to start with, in view of the many disappointments we had experienced in the past, of various kinds.

"Until we get our sea legs under us," I explained to him, "we'll just feel our way into this selling game.''

The relative was most delighted to hear that we were both going to join his sales staff and he wanted to send us a couple of hundred clocks; but Jim told him to keep the clocks and deliver them direct to our customers, as the orders came in.

"The big salesman," said Jim, "never carries samples, even. But I'll pick one up from him this afternoon, and we'll take it with us to-night. We'd better not resign from The Star Weekly until we've got a couple of hundred sales to our credit in our spare time, and anyway, it wouldn't be fair to them to just walk out this suddenly.''

Three blocks west of us is a nice district we call the "butler belt" where dwell a lot of comfortable people who zing past our neighborhood in their big dark cars. We decided to start our campaign there. Before setting out, Jimmie set the sample clock up. It was a curious looking clock, modernistic to say the least of it. But after all, most clocks are pretty old-fashioned looking, and even a slight departure from the conventional clock is startling. Jim plugged into a lamp socket and we watched with delight the smooth, silent way the hands moved. We set its alarm and heard its shrill clarion, enough to get a man out of bed and dress him before he knew what had happened. We studied all the various connections for burglar alarms, rain indicators, light-turner-out, and so forth, but decided not to waste valuable sales hours by hooking her all up.

With a cool sense of courage, we drove three blocks and stopped before a large and nicely lighted home where figures within moved against the lights.

Smiling easily and making as if to walk right in when the maid opened the door, Jimmie said:

"Could we see Mr. Mmmffffzzzth, please?"

And in we walked.

The maid hurried away, and presently a stout, baldish man in his shirtsleeves and carrying a newspaper, came into the hall.

"How do you do?" we cried, shaking hands.

"What is this?" asked the gentleman, whose name, we learned, was Mr. McDucky.

"Wait till you see it?" said Jim, laying his hat down and carrying the parcelled clock into the living room. Mr. McDucky and I followed, all eagerness.

Jim untied the package, and set the clock on the mantel. Smiling in excitement, he smoothly and without hesitation ran the cord to a wall plug, and set her in motion.

"Now," said Jim, "to look at, you would think this was just an electric clock."

And before Mr. McDucky's speechless gaze, he standing there still holding the open newspaper hanging in his hand, Jim put the clock through its marvellous paces. It range various alarms, short and long, which brought Mrs. McDucky and three daughters from all parts of the house to look. Jim explained the rain indicator, the burglar alarm, the light-turner-out, and all the many useful attachments of this wonder clock of the age.

"Hook her up," said Mr. McDucky.

So Jimmie and I, taking off our coats, and going by the sheet of instructions enclosed, ran wires and clamps to window fasteners and door locks. Mr. McDucky sent over to the hardware store for more wire. We unscrewed electric light push-button plates and did exactly as the directions told us with the wires attached to the gadgets inside the fixtures. But something was amiss, and even with the help of Mr. McDucky, who was just as interested and got himself as mussed and dusty as either of us, we could not make it turn off the lights or ring the burglar alarm, or indicate rain, though it was raining cats and dogs.

By the time we folded it all up and packed it back in its cardboard box, it was getting towards bedtime, and Mrs. McDucky and the girls brought in coffee and sandwiches and we sat around the living room while Mr. McDucky told us about his business, which was the mining business.

With Heads Ringing

"I deal," he explained, "in futures. I work, you might say, with those real heroes of the great mining industry, the pioneer prospectors. So, many times a year, I go north and actually visit the ground where these men are toiling, doing the genuine and most deserving part of the whole game. Yet how little they get out of it."

"True," we agreed, via ham and pickle sandwiches.

"I've been in the mining game all my life," said Mr. McDucky, "yet I never owned a share of stock. I buy properties. Straight from the prospectors."

And he told us about the romance and thrill and what interested him less, but interested him just the same, the fortunes to be made in thus dealing with the raw materials, you might say, of Canada's greatest industry.

After his wife and daughters had gone upstairs, Mr. McDucky, after a thought of silence, finally laughed and said:

"It's funny you dropping in this way tonight! I was just sitting here running over in my mind who I would let in on a few units of what appears to be the greatest find of my life and one of the greatest gold mines in the history of the whole country."

And there, before our astonished faces, Mr. McDucky brought out and laid, rows and rows of samples of ore rock, and some pieces that appeared to be solid gold. Photographs of wild north country, prospectors working in rocky trenches, shacks, trestles, drilling outfits.

"You see," explained Mr. McDucky, flushed like a child, "I couldn't let the whole gang in on this. They'd crowd me out of it in a week. But as I always say, I like to let new blood into the mining game."

And before we knew where we were, Jimmie and I were the proud possessors of ten units each of McDucky Syndicate shares, merely signed our names and not a cent of cash changing hands, it being as Mr. McDucky said, unlucky to pay cash after business hours.

And we drove home, our heads singing with golden chimes and the songs of whipporrwills and the clang of prospector picks upon the vast igneous rocks of Canada's fabulous north.

"Hey," said Jimmie, as he let me out at my house. "how about the clock? You take it, will you?"

"I really don't need it," I said "I have clocks all over the house."

"But not electric clocks," said Jim. "You take it. I can get another one."

"No, no," I insisted, "not at all. Jimmie if I need one, you can get it for me sometime."

"It's a great clock," said Jim. "You ought to have one. Wholesale?"

"No, no," I assured him. "It's yours by rights."

But I saw it, on the back seat under the rug, when we drove down in the morning.

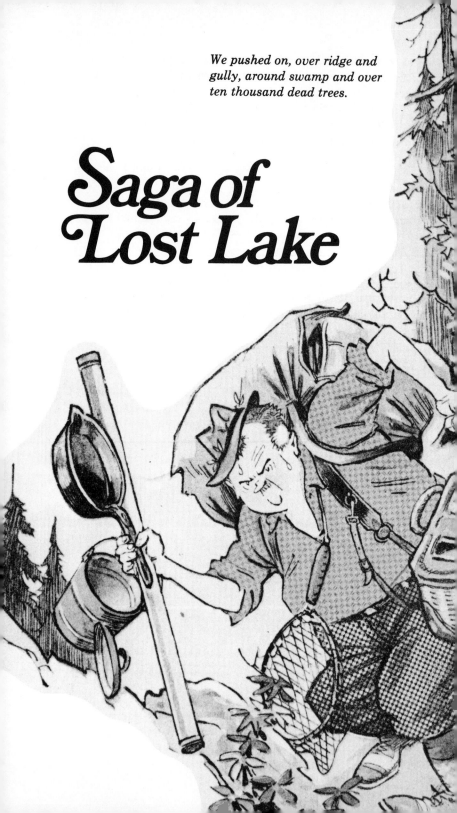

We pushed on, over ridge and gully, around swamp and over ten thousand dead trees.

Saga of Lost Lake

"T HIS," said Jimmie Frise, "is the worst year for fishing we've ever had."

"Is it any wonder," I demanded "with fresh thousands taking up fishing every year and fresh miles of highway being built farther and farther into the wilds, every season?"

"All our old haunts are ruined," said Jim.

"Yet we," I accused, "thought it was swell when they completed the cement highways to all our favorite spots."

"Even Algonquin Park has a highway into it now," sighed Jim.

"Canada's richest asset," I declared, "is the tourist traffic. It's the strangest export business in the world. It brings in three hundred million dollars per annum net cash. And all it takes out is snapshots.''

"We're selling our birthright," pronounced Jim solemnly, "for a mess of pottage. When we have ripped our country wide open for the tourist trade, when we've criss-crossed it with highways and looted all our lakes, and made hot dog groves of all our forests and nothing remains but an empty fraud, and all the annual three hundred millions have vanished, as millions do, into thin air, what will we have left?"

"We'll have had a good time while it lasted," I pointed out. "Three hundred million a year is mighty sweet money."

"We'll have rotting highways running through barren and useless waste," said Jim. "Our tourist trade goes into a country unfit for anything but playing in. It has no soil for farming. It is no good for reforesting. When the fish are gone and the wied aspect vanished, the tourist will leave us holding the empty bag."

"Why, Jim," I laughed, "within ten years, the American tourists are going to be working their way into our Arctic. Already, hundreds of Americans are going every summer into the Albany watershed, running into Hudson Bay. Already, thousands of Americans are taking hunting trips into the Yukon and the northern Rockies. Our tourist trade is good for another hundred years, with that wild, unexplored Arctic up there."

"And what about us poor guys," demanded Jim, "that can't afford to go two thousand miles north? Is fishing in Canada only to be for wealthy Americans?"

"Oh, they'll stock up the local waters," I assured him. "It's all a question of demand. As soon as the fishing gets bad enough, there will be a violent uproar, and the government will go nutty planting fish. They'll plant fish the way they have been building highways lately, or the way they do anything else to please the public. A government's real job, after all, isn't governing. It's pleasing the public. They govern for a couple of years. Then they wake up with a violent start and realize that pleasing the public is the whole thing. That's the way we'll get fish down around these parts. The day is coming when it won't be safe to go for a paddle on any water in the older part of the country. The fish will be a menace."

"Tame fish," sneered Jim. "Liver-fed fish."

"You'll be glad enough to hook them," I assured him.

"I'll be an old man," said Jim. "Too feeble to go fishing."

Reaction in Pioneering
"If we had any gumption," I stated, "we'd not be sitting

here letting the Americans have all the fun going up the Albany and the Winisk. We'd be going ourselves. What's the matter with us Canadians? Why do we insist on puddling around near home, when there is simply incredible wild fishing a day or two north? Are we getting soft? Where is the pioneer spirit that, only fifty years ago, was part and parcel of every Canadian's character."

"I guess," said Jim, "that there is a sort of reaction in this pioneer spirit business. Pioneering gets kind of exhausted after three or four generations. We belong to one of the two or three generations that are resting up after the ordeal. Then maybe our grandchildren will feel the pioneer spirit creeping back into them again."

"By which time," I pointed out, "the good fishing will be exhausted in the Arctic."

"Then our grandchildren," said Jim, "will run across to fish in Siberia and northern Russia as carelessly as we go up to Lake Nipissing."

"Ah, boy," I sighed, "I wish I could go to a lake my Uncle Ed took me into when I was a kid. I was about sixteen, I guess. Talk about bass fishing."

"Where was the lake?" asked Jim.

"It is the most lost lake," I declared, "imaginable. In fact, we called it Lost Lake. It's still there. It is miles from any human habitation. It is a twenty-mile walk over the wildest, rockiest country anywhere in Canada."

"Twenty miles," said Jim. "Whew! Your Uncle Ed must have been a tough guy."

"Tough is right," I agreed. "He was a pioneer. I can see him yet, with his great big packsack on his back, full of tent and grub and tackle, climbing over those wild rocks like a goat. I've never been so weary in all my life, yet I was a strong husky kid of sixteen."

"What about the fishing?" asked Jim.

"Lost Lake," I began happily, "is about half a mile wide and four miles long. It is a great bed of glacial gravel set down amidst the most God-forsaken rock in the world. It never was lumbered because there isn't anything but scrub will grow on it. There isn't half an acre of soil within 30 miles. Yet that long, narrow lake, full of bright gravel and boulders and reefs, is simply alive with bass up to six pounds."

"Oh, oh," said Jim.

"Jim," I said, "my Uncle Ed was a fly fisherman. No bait, no worms, crawfish or frogs for him. Just common trout flies, on little four-ounce rods. He taught me to fly fish. We made a raft of cedar logs. We drifted about that heavenly lake for five days. Every cast, with those tiny little trout flies, a great whacking big bass, from four to six pounds. We put on two flies. We got two bass to a cast. We filed off the barbs of the fly hooks. We caught hundreds of bass and threw them all back except the ones we needed to eat. We never even brought any out.''

"Have you never gone back?'' demanded Jim.

"I intended to go back the next year,'' I said, "but I started to Varsity. Then I kept putting it off year by year, as I got into that silly age around 20, when you never seem to be able to keep your mind on anything really important. Then the war came. And then Uncle Ed got rheumatism.''

Engraved on My Memory

"Is it far away?'' asked Jim.

"Far enough,'' I said. "You go to Sudbury, and then in by train about 30 miles. You get off at a section man's house and then walk in 20 miles. No road, no trail. Just across the wild barren rock, working by landmarks.''

"You'd have forgotten them,'' thought Jim, "by now.''

"Never,'' I cried, "to my dying day. It's engraved on my memory like the path I took to school as a child. Every once in a while, over the long years. I have renewed my memory by going, in my imagination, over every foot of that trip. First you head for a distant sort of ridge or pinnacle of rocks, far in the distance. You can't go wrong. Then, from this pinnacle, you can see, miles ahead, a series of great muskeg swamps with broken ridges of rock rising between them. You follow that series of ridges between the muskeg swamps, as straight as Yonge St., and they bring you smack out on to Lost Lake.''

"Boy,'' said Jim grimly. "Let's go. Let's go.''

"Jim?'' I cried, "will you?''

"Let's go,'' repeated Jim with a sort of anguish.

"It's a terrible walk,'' I said, "twenty miles. With all our duffle. Tent and grub and tackle and pots and pans.''

"Man,'' shouted Jim, "a lake like that, lost amidst all this exploitation and ruin of lakes. A lake like that, within an overnight journey in a sleeping car with hordes of people going hundreds of miles beyond to fish waters already overrun with other fishermen. How do you know it hasn't been found out by now?''

"How would it be found out?'' I demanded. "Nobody but Uncle Ed and two other men knew of it. And who would walk 20 miles nowadays in this age of satin-smooth highways and motor cars and outboard motors? This is a soft, padded age. The modern sportsman won't go any place he can't sit on a cushion all the way.''

"One good fill of fishing," crooned Jim, "one regular orgy of fishing, and I'll be content to hang up my rods and let my grandchildren go to the Arctic.''

"It's a go," I announced.

And we sat straight down and proceeded to examine the calendar and then drew up lists of duffle and supplies.

We decided to spend four days on the lake. One full day to walk in and one full day to walk out. We debated whether to take Jim's little wedge tent or my big silk one, and we concluded that as we were no longer chickens, it might be as well to be comfortable.

"This business of going light," said Jim, "is all very well in your twenties. But at our age, we've got to get our rest.''

So we wrote and rewrote our camping lists, which, as anybody knows, is the better part of camping. The tent and our two sleeping bags would go into a joint dunnage bag which we would carry between us. Each of us would have our packsacks, containing clothes, tackle, and all the things needful to a happy outing. Pots and pans we would distribute between us pro rata. The grub we would divide equally and stow in our packsacks.

And Saturday night, we left for Sudbury by sleeper, arriving early in the morning and continuing by day coach some miles out to the section men's shack where the unmarked trail to Lost Lake began,

The section man's shack, which had been young and red and fresh when I was sixteen was now no more than a worn old shed in which some railway ties were stored and even the rusty old tin cases in its neighborhood looked as if this had been no human habitation for many a long year. It was no longer even a section house, just a relic of a shanty, faded and old.

"Jim," I declared, as the train sped off leaving us alone with our duffle bags, "this is wonderful. I feared we might even find a village where this section house had stood. But look - it's only a ruin. Lost Lake has stayed lost, for sure.''

From a little rocky eminence handy, we could see the remote whitish rock ridges or pinnacles far to the northwest, just as I had described them.

"It's a good ten miles to them, Jim," I said. "By keeping to ridges and high ground, we never lose sight of them. We'll take all morning, just to reach them.''

But it took more than the morning. I don't know how far a lumberjack carries his packsack. Probably from the railway station to the boarding house, maybe. A distance of 75 yards in most lumberjack communities. Even the pioneers used oxen. Certainly no pioneer ever carried a packsack ten miles. Or else why did it take a hundred years for the pioneers to work north a hundred miles?

As I said before, it was a wild and rugged country, and a number of swamps had moved or side-slipped, during the past 30 years, for I found any number of swamps where there had been none the last time. A swamp is a thing you have to go around. And often you have to feel your way around it, making many false tries, this way and that.

At noon, the delectable white pinnacles were still white and remote. We halted for lunch and got out our sleeping bags to lie on for a little rest. We rested until four o'clock and then pushed on. By six p.m., the pinnacles were less distant and less white, but none the less too far away for a couple of pioneers without oxen to reach by dark. So finding a pleasant little swampy pond in the middle of a muskeg, we made camp, and boiled muddy tea and sent to bed on ill-made brush beds, and muttered each other awake all night.

In the morning, we went through our packsacks and made a cache in a tree of all the articles, many of them costly if not valuable, to lighten our loads and to be picked up on the way out. They are there forever, I fear.

Thus, lightened, we struck camp and pushed on, over ridge and gully and around swamp and over ten thousand dead trees until at noon we reached the high ridge from which, stretching far to the west, we beheld, as I had foretold, the series of dark swamps between which wended bare bleak wastes of rock. But these wastes of rock were open and grim and barren and easy, and in slow stages between heavy rests, during which our eyeballs protruded and our kidneys ached and our legs grew numb and our arches fell and our toe-balls scalded, we went out across those hog-backs of rock amidst endless wastes of swamp, straight as a ship sails towards Lost Lake.

It's A Mirage - A Delusion

At five p.m. from the highest of these heaves of rock, we glimpsed a bit of blue.

"Water," I cried. "It's Lost Lake."

And with a sort of spiritual, if not physical, second wind, we pushed on. Jim holding one end of the tent bag and I the other, and clanking with our pots and pans like Mrs. Finnigan's cows, and over seven last great hills of rock we came at last to the very last, and there at our feet, half a mile wide and four miles long, lay Lost Lake.

"What's that?" gasped Jim, softly lowering his packsack from his long and limber back.

It was music.

We eased our weary baggage down, and listened.

"It's 'Love 'Em and Leave 'Em'," I said. "This week's number on the Hit Parade."

"Look," said Jim pointing.

In the gloaming, lights twinkled at almost regular intervals along the distant shores of Lost Lake.

"Cottages," I said huskily, "It's a mirage. It's a delusion. We're suffering from explorer's exhaustion."

Around the point we stood on, a canoe came, and from it the music we had heard rose with increasing volume.

It was a boy and a girl, with a portable victrola between them in their cushioned ease. When they beheld us in the semi-dark, frozen beside our packsacks and dunnage bags, festooned with our pails and pans, they too froze, staring.

"Hello," I called hollowly.

The boy paddled cautiously nearer.

"Is this Lost Lake?" I demanded hoarsely.

"No, sir," said the boy. "This is Golden Sand Lake."

"It used to be called Lost Lake," the girl piped up, "before the highway came by. I've heard my dad speak of it by that name."

"Highway?" croaked Jimmie.

"The highway," said the boy, "just along the other side, see?"

Three cars, lights just turned on, sailed smoothly along the far side of the lake, headed inexorably northward, northward.

"Any bass in this lake?" I asked lightly.

"Not now," said the girl, "but my daddy has one stuffed in our cottage, he got the first year we were in here before I was born, and it weighed six pounds."

"Do you suppose?" I inquired, "we could get a lift across the lake to the highway side?"

"I'll go and get our launch," said the boy, immediately. "I'll take you across and you can get a bus. There's a bus every two hours, both ways."

"That's swell," said Jim.

So we sat down on our duffle and waited for the launch, watching the car lights streaming past on the far side, and not speaking at all, but just thinking and thinking.

The Evening's Fishing

"**W**HAT is it," asked Jimmie Frise, snuggling deeper behind the steering wheel, "that makes us so nuts about fishing?"

"It's like having red hair," I explained, "or being able to sing. It's just born in us."

"I'm not so sure," said Jim. "Here we are, heading north at a high rate of speed for the opening of the bass season. We've spent every week-end in May and June trout fishing, to the neglect of our business and our families. We've spent far more money on it than any budget normally allows for pleasure."

"Fishing only lasts," I pointed out, "from May first to the middle of October. Five and a half measly months."

"Most people," stated Jim, "take two weeks holiday in the

The skiff curved alongside and Simon, all grins like a child, turned the engine off.

summer and let it go at that. Here we not only take two weeks but about twenty week-ends."

"Everybody does something with their week-ends," I countered. "Golfing, driving in the country. Lots of them take trips south."

"Most of them," corrected Jim, " just stay home."

"Well," I agreed, " it's a free country. And if a man takes more pleasure staying home on week-ends and saving his money, that's his pleasure. I would no more think of interfering with him staying home than I would permit him to interfere with me going away."

"What I mean is," said Jim, "those who stay home feel that they can't really afford to go busting off on trips."

"They're welcome to feel anyway they like," I admitted happily, "so long as by deed or word or facial expression they don't attempt to interfere with my way of thinking. These people who stay home on week-ends are probably looking forward to a comfortable old age. That's a form of amusement I have no use for. Comfortable old age! Imagine guys in good health sitting around all Saturday and Sunday greedily looking forward to a comfortable old age. Of all the disgusting habits."

"I'd say it was mighty good sense. Far-sighted." said Jim.

"Short-sighted, you mean," I insisted. "Can't they see all around them that old age is hardly ever comfortable? It's full of aches and pains. They're so fat they can't breathe or so thin they hurt all over even lying in bed. All the things that have happened to them in their lives seem to pile on top of them in the end. They've eaten too heartily or have got round-shouldered at sedentary jobs. What they thought all their lives was just being careful turns out in the end to be only mean and it shows in their faces. Unless you die when you're about twenty-five life is always disappointing and the longer you live the more disappointed with it you grow. That is unless you go fishing or something."

"You've got the worst philosophy I ever heard," said Jim loudly and stepping on the gas.

"Well, show me something better than fishing," I retorted.

"It's the most selfish pleasure on earth," stated Jim. "A golfer only leaves his family for a few hours and an occasional evening. But a fisherman runs away Friday night and never turns up until late Sunday night or early Monday morning, looking sunburned and guilty."

"His family are glad to be rid of him," I said.

"Even week-end trips cost money," said Jim. "A man runs away with a lot of money fishing."

"I suppose it would be better," I sneered, "if he were to save it little by little until the next depression. Surely nobody in the whole world believes in saving money any more."

"Aw", scoffed Jimmie.

"All right; all I say is, anybody is a fool to save," I assured him. "And of all the ways of not saving. I think fishing is the best."

"And," questioned Jim, "when you are old and can't go fishing any more and all your money is gone, how will you feel?"

"Far better than most of my generation," I declared. "For I can say, 'Here I am without any money, but I've had a hell of a good time,' And the rest of the inmates of the poorhouse will be hunched up, their hands clasped between their boney knees, moaning, 'Here I am without any money and look how I've suffered.' I bet I'll be the happiest old guy in the old men's home. That's something to look forward to."

"I'm looking forward," stated Jim, "to some swell fishing in about three hours. We'll have the evening from at least six o'clock: we ought to get our limit of six bass before dark in dear old Lake Skeebawa."

"What a lake," I agreed. "And to think we have it practically to ourselves."

"What I like about Skeebawa," said Jim, " is there are no motor boats on it. No engines humming and snorting and putting. No oil fouling the pure water. Just a little secret lake that seems to have escaped the march of progress."

"What I hate about motor boats," I said, "is that they allow wholly undeserving people, fat, cushion-sitting fish hogs, to race around the lake taking in only the very best fishing spots. Good fishing belongs to those who are willing to take the trouble to win it."

"Of course, our guides do the paddling," reminded Jim.

"Good old Simon and good old Sandy." I cried. "Will they be glad to see us? I've brought Simon a couple of my old pipes and a pound of that cheap tobacco he likes."

"I've brought Sandy that hunting knife I got for Christmas," said Jim. "It'll make a big hit with Sandy."

"This makes ten years," I mused, "that Simon and Sandy have paddled us the rounds of Skeebawa."

"They're grand old boys," said Jim. "Let's see: we'll do the usual round. We'll take to the left from the boathouse and cast all along that rush bed. Then cut across to Simon's Point and fish the shoal for say half an hour. Then along those lily pads on far side37C for say half an hour. Then along those Lily pads on the far side and so home by dark. We can do that in three hours."

A Disturbing Sound

"Easy," I agreed, turning to take stock of my various items of tackle, rods, boxes in the back seat. "What are you going to start with?"

"Red and white plug," said Jim.

"I think I'll start with that copper casting spoon," I considered. "It'll be a bright evening and after the hot spell the bass won't be any too frisky."

"Six bass apiece," sang Jimmie, giving the gas to her. "And then in the dark walking up to Andy's cottage for one of Mrs. Andy's glorious fried bass dinners."

"Then sitting out under the stars listening to the whippoor-wills," I joined in, "and talking slow and lazy with old Simon and Andy about last winter and how they worked in the lumber camps and what they trapped and the big lake trout they caught through the ice."

"And," sighed Jim, "going to bed knowing that to-morrow we have the whole glorious long day, from misty sunrise to moonlit dark, just casting, casting, casting."

We fell silent and watched the long road rolling under us and the bright summer fields and the farmers already in their hay. And, thinking the idle thoughts of the true angler, we watched the woods grow thicker, and darker with the northering miles, and a tingle come into the air, and the smell of the lakes, the little lakes, come cool and secret, through the summer.

We reached at last, both of us eager and sitting up fresh, the road that goes to Skeebawa, loveliest of the little lily-margined lakes, and wound down through familiar narrowing roads of cedar jungles and high stumpy barrens and aisled forests of maple and oak seeing with joyous hearts the narrowing, the roughening that meant the ever nearer approach to the little lost water where Simon and Sandy would probably be waiting for us at the old broken rail fence at the turn down, as in all the happy past.

We reached the fence at last, both of us emitting ceremonial shouts and hurrahs. But neither Simon nor Sandy was waiting for us at the usual spot. Down the sandy ruts towards Sandy's cabin, we turned.

"Been a heavy car in here to-day," said Jim briefly.

"Hm," said I. "Of course there are other guests always. But Simon will always save his canoe for me.

"One thing is certain," agreed Jim.

Over the knoll we rose and, as usual, stopped the car to feast our gaze on wrinkled blue Skeebawa spread below us. Jim turned off the engine and said,

"AaaaaHHHH."

A curious horrible sound came to ours ears. It was the distant drone and whine of a powerful outboard motor engine.

"Jim," I cried.

Jim snatched at the key and started the car.

"Sandy never," Jim said, "never would have bought an engine. He couldn't afford one,for one thing."

"Let's get there," I said, and took hold for the bumps down the few hundred yards of sandy ruts to the cabin.

Mrs. Sandy came out as we drove in the yard, wiping her hands on her apron and waving to us.

"Mrs. Sandy," I said, leaping out, "is that an engine?"

"It sure is," said Mrs. Sandy delightedly. "An old gent arrived last night with a trailer and his own boat on it. See, there?"

Under the pines where our car usually rested was a big rich car and attached to it a trailer such as big skiffs are carried on. It was a rich man's car.

"Where are the boys?" demanded Jim.

"Out with him," said Mrs. Sandy. "What a time they're having. That boat skims, so it does. Just skims. They've been all around the lake half a dozen times and got no end of bass, but he puts them all back over the six he's allowed by the law."

"Mrs. Sandy," I said, "didn't the boys know we'd be here?"

"Certainly they know," she cried. "Of course they did and come in and I'll take you to your room."

"But Mrs. Sandy," said Jim, "we were hoping to go right out. For the evening's fishing."

"The canoes are right where you'll find them," said Mrs. Sandy. "He's paying the boys ten dollars a day to ride in that boat with him. Ten dollars a day. My, he's a rich man."

"Mrs. Sandy," said Jim, "is there nobody to paddle us?"

"Simon tried all night nearly," said she, "to get one of his nephews, but they were busy. The boys said you wouldn't mind paddling yourself to-night and they'll have some nephews for you in the morning.''

"In the morning?'' said I. "Is the rich gentleman staying?''

"Staying?'' cried Mrs. Sandy. "He's crazy about the place. He says he's been looking for it all his life. He's telegraphed all his friends ...''

"Ooooohhh,'' moaned Jim, and I joined in and harmonized my groan.

"Why gentlemen,'' cried Mrs. Sandy, "the lake's full of fish. He says he never saw such fishing. He's hooked forty if he's hooked one. And him and the boys, in that skimmer, has just been scooting from one good spot to the next all day long, wasting no time... He's taking me for a spin in it after dinner tonight.''

"Indeed,'' said Jim.

"Let's get on the water,'' I muttered.

Hurriedly we carried our duffle to the house, where Mrs. Sandy showed us to the room next to our old one. Our old room strangely packed with foreign duffle, scads of it, rod cases, big leather and canvas bags, expensive-looking tweed coats, rugs, tackle boxes flung about.

"Can't we have our old room?'' I demanded.

"He's paying twenty dollars a day,'' whispered Mrs. Sandy tremendously, "twenty dollars a day for this room and he says he won't give a cent less.''

We dropped our bags in a little room with a slanting ceiling and stuffy smell, a room I had not even glanced into in all the years. We changed into old clothes, snatched up rods and boxes and walked down in the evening to the ramshackel boathouse and got out Simon's red canoe.

"I'll paddle,'' I growled so determinedly that Jim didn't even haggle.

Silently I drove the canoe along towards the long rush beds while Jim mounted his reel and tied on his favorite red and white bass plug. As we cast along, the drone and snarl of the engine resounded from the far end of the lake, starting and stopping, as we pictured just which best spots this old devil was fishing in turn. We fished the two hundred yeards of rush beds without a single strike. Not a swirl. In past years we each always took two bass of this rush bed. Two and three pounders.

"Simon,'' I said, "has probably had him along here.''

"Sandy, too," said Jim shortly.

Far down the quieting lake we heard distant merry shouts and the familiar music of a man into a fish. It sounded like a big one.

I paddled Jim heavily across to the boulder point and set him just the right distance to cast over the shoals. Ten casts, not a bass. Twenty casts, not a bass.

"He's probably been over this ground a dozen times to-day," I suggested.

We heard the distant engine start up and around the far point came the smoothly skimming skiff. The water was still and like a creature of evil the skiff came boring and arrowing up the lake. I heard the loud calls as Simon and Sandy saw us, and the skiff turned and came for us, racketing the echoes of the quiet hills of Skeebawa and breaking the peaceful lake into waves and wash. In an instant the skiff curved alongside us and Simon, all grins like a child, turned the engine off.

In the middle, easy and quiet, sat a skinny little man. He was beyond seventy. He was wiry and bright eyed. In his hand he held the most expensive type of rod and it was mounted with one of those twenty-five dollar reels.

"Good evening, gentlemen," he said, as our craft touched sides gently. "The boys tell me this is your private little heaven. I hope you will welcome a new and unworthy angel?"

And Jimmie and I, a little stiffly perhaps, welcomed him and denied it was any private heaven and that all lakes were public property and anybody who cared could come on them, and then we drifted off on the pretext of having just another couple of dozen casts at a special spot where some cedars hung out over the water.

"We done that," cried Simon. "We done it twice this morning and three times this afternoon."

And with a flourish he started the engine and away they soared for the cabin.

"Jim," I said, "I can't stay.. I can't even stay the night."

"Me, too," said Jim, reeling up.

And we slunk in and packed our stuff amid the lovely odor of frying bass while the stranger sat at feast. We told the boys and Mrs. Sandy we had just dropped in for old time's sake, but that we had to meet a gang of friends at another lake forty miles up.

And into the night, directionless, not knowing whither, we drove, back out the old twisting road.

"The only thing a man can do," said Jim, "is save his money

and work like a fool when he's young so as to be able to go fishing when he is old.''

"It's the only way to compete nowadays," I agreed.

"You never said a truer word," said Jim, relapsing into the silence that befitted the dark and pine-girt night.

The following stories originally appeared in the Star Weekly *on these dates:*

INSULATION – October 30, 1937

SKUNKED AGAIN – December 11, 1937

UP WHERE THE NORTH BEGINS –
January 8, 1938

SCALPED IN THE RUSH – March 5, 1938

WEAK-ENDERS – June 11, 1938

SOME OTHER TIME – May 21, 1938

"With a rending and crackling sound, my feet went into space ..."

Insulation

"**C**ANADIANS," said Jimmie Frise, "should have solved this climate generations ago."

"It's full of novelty," I admitted.

"Either," said Jim, "they should have worked out some solution of how to keep warm in Canada or else given the silly country up."

"There is no accounting," I pointed out, "for the funny places you will find the human race. Take Eskimos, for instance. I have often wondered, not as to why they ever went to the Arctic, but why they stayed there."

"Or Negroes," said Jim, "in the Congo jungles. All they had to do was keep on walking and they'd have come out at Cape Colony, which they tell me is a lovely, pleasant climate."

"Eskimos," I insisted, "are sillier. All they had to do was take their canoes and travel along the shore around down by Labrador, and where would they have come out? Why, Maryland, or Virginia or some of those nice regions where the winter is never cold and the summer is never hot."

"I don't mind the summer,"said Jim. "You can always find a shady spot. But what can you do in the winter? Even if you do keep the fires roaring, there is always a cold blast ready to wham into you, from an opened door or a crack of the window."

"Now, you take the Scotch," I pursued. "Scotland is a hard, flinty country, full of fog and dismal purple hills. It is steep and misty and grim. It sticks up into the Arctic ocean, and its birds have queer, wild cries and its crops are harsh and few. Yet no race on earth have written such love songs to their land as the Scotch."

"The Scotch," explained Jim, "have been working South into England for several hundred years and they write these songs about bonnie Scotland in the hope that the English will go north and so leave them more room in Surrey and Kent."

"How did the Scotch," I demanded, "originally get into Scotland? That's the puzzle."

"How did the Canadians get into Canada, is worse," stated Jim. "The only explanation is that our ancestors were kind of dumb."

"You hate the cold, don't you?" I suggested.

"Heat," declared Jim, "is so silly. It goes up. With a force as absolute and furious as the law of gravity, heat shoots up. With a power vastly greater than the greatest anti-aircraft gun on earth, the heat shoots straight up."

"What of it?" I enquired.

"It's so silly," protested Jim, peevishly. "Heat is the one thing all nature loves. Heat is the most desirable thing in the whole world, yet is is always struggling insanely to escape. Where? Into upper space, where, in the ultimate chill, it is consumed and wiped out."

"It's all according to physical law," I elucidated.

Loveliest Thing on Earth

"That doesn't make it any less silly," insisted Jim, "Why doesn't cold go up and heat fall? I have been thinking about this business of heat rising lately, and the more I think of it, the more irritated I get."

"There's really nothing we can do about it," I pointed out.

"Even so," stated Jim, "I have the right to be irritated, haven't I? Heat is certainly the most desirable thing in all the universe. Food, love, sport, movies, music, nothing compares with heat as the loveliest thing on earth. When heat comes, the whole of nature springs to life. When heat goes, nature dies. When warmth comes stealing, the dead earth grows green, flowers bloom, lambs are born, the fields grow rich with life and food. When warmth begins to steal away, the leaves fall, the fields grow brown, the birds fly away, the world all but dies. Cold therefore is the hateful thing. If heat is the most desirable thing in the universe, cold is the most undesirable. Cold is hateful, cruel, vicious, wicked.''

"So what?'' I proffered.

"Nothing,'' sighed Jim, "only I think it is ridiculous the way heat keeps rushing up. The stupid thing. Think of it. Think of all the trouble we go to, millions of men digging down into the bowels of the earth for coal, toiling in remote forests to chop down trees, creating whole civilizations around oil wells to drive shafts miles deep into the earth, what for? To get fuel so that all of us can make fires to keep warm. And what does the heat do?''

"Goes up,'' I contributed.

"Exactly,'' cried Jim. "Doesn't that make you mad?''

"I sort of expect it, I guess,'' I said lamely, because normally I love to share people's indignations.

"I've been fretting over this thing,'' confessed Jim, "because I've either got to sell my house or install a new heating plant or else insulate. I was all right so long as I stuck to selling the house or putting in a new furnace. That was just a simple matter. The house was cold. So I either had to get a bigger furnace or else sell the place and get a warm house. Then these insulation experts got me.''

"Ah,'' I sympathized.

"The word got around,'' said Jim, "that I was thinking of doing something about my house, and three salesmen called on me. They represent three different kinds of insulation. Some of it you blow in. Others you lay in the cotton batting. Others you cement in, in blocks or bricks.''

"Snow is a good insulator,'' I pointed out. "As soon as the snow falls, you notice the house gets warmer.''

"As a matter of fact,'' said Jim, "one of the salesmen told me that as good an insulator as there is in the world is common ashes. Fine ashes like wood ashes. Just spread a three or four-inch layer of ashes up amongst the joists between your ceiling and the roof, and you've got as good as you can buy.''

"That was nice of him'' I agreed.

Its One Impulse is to Vanish

"But it was these birds who poisoned my mind about heat," said Jim. "I had no idea the way heat acts, until they came and sat in my living room after supper, and with gestures and oratory showed me the way heat vanishes. Why, do you know that heat will go right through a solid plaster ceiling as easy as water goes through sand? Do you know that heat is a ray? Do you know that the minute heat is born, its one and only impulse is to drive through solid plaster, mortar, brick, stone, and even steel, and vanish in the direction of the Milky Way?"

"Don't get excited," I soothed him.

"Well, it gets me down," muttered Jim. "It haunts me. All I can think of is me piling coal on furnaces and carrying ashes for the past twenty years, for what?"

"You'd think you were the only person who ever owned a furnace," I laughed.

"One thing I'm going to do," said Jim, "whether I put in a bigger furnace or whether I sell, I'm going to insulate anyway, just to get even with heat."

"Just to get even?" I expostulated.

"The way this insulation works," explained Jim, "is, it makes a fool of heat. This insulation is all tangled up. It is like one of those trick mazes in the Midway at the Exhibition. Heat goes proudly into this insulation, and before it knows where it is, it is back in the room where it started. It gets lost. It grows bewildered. The longer it struggles and twists in amongst the crooked molecules and atoms of this insulation, the wearier it gets, until at last it gives up trying, and falls back, exhauted, right into your living room."

"It sounds simple," I admitted.

"Heat is in the habit," explained Jim, "of going straight through the honest particles of brick and wood and stuff. It is like going along a path, winding a little but straight enough. When heat hits this insulation, it is like trying to follow a cow path or rabbit tracks in a swamp. Heat gets confused. It becomes lost. Night falls. Heat starves to death."

"Hurray," I cried.

"You ought to insulate," stated Jim.

"No," I decreed, "I come of an old Ontario family. My father was born in a log cabin. I come of good old stuff. I feel I owe it to my forehears to be a little uncomfortable in the winter. What kind of insulation are you going to use?"

"If I could get anybody to help me," said Jim, looking out the window, "I would do it myself. There is a kind of insulation you can get in bags. It is light as feathers. It comes in pillows, sort of. Pillows of this fluffy stuff. You just climb up through the trap door leading into your roof, and spread these pillows all over the rafters. It wouldn't take two hours."

"It's an expert's job," I supposed.

"Expert," said Jim. "A guy in overalls. And he will charge me $12 just for the laying."

"I'd help you in a minute," I assured Jim, "if I weren't so clumsy at those practical jobs."

The Handicap of Size

"As a matter of fact," said Jim, "I was half hoping you would offer to help me. The space under my roof is so small, it will take a small man, like yourself, to do it. The salesman I showed it to said that very thing. It will take a small man to do this, he said."

"There are lots of times," I informed him, "when is is an advantage to be small. And other times, it is a disadvantage."

"There is a little square trap-door," said Jim, "in one of the bedroom closets. You get on the step-ladder and push this lip up and there you are, right up in the raw rafters. I tried to get up in there, but it is so low, there is hardly room for me to squat, much less stoop. But you could reach every part of it."

"I don't like the sound of it," I stated. "After all, twelve dollars..."

"It isn't the money," Jim assured me. "It's the personal feeling of the thing. I want to feel I am personally skunking heat. And I feel fortunate in having among my friends a man of small size and big heart who..."

"If you put it that way, Jim," I said.

And the deal was done.

Ten bags of this stuff was piled in the pretty bedroom when we arrived to do the job. We set the ladder in the clothes closet and Jim climbed up and pushed aside the small square trap-door in the ceiling. He hoisted himself up and his legs vanished. I handed him up the flashlight and followed him.

We were in a queer, rough little place of rafters and raw wood, a tiny barn-like, weird little shadow room, in curious contrast to the bright, civilized boudoirs beneath us. It was stuffy and chill.

Scantlings a foot and a half apart were the only floor, because the lath and plaster of the ceiling of the rooms below were fastened directly to these scantlings.

"All you've got to do," said Jim, shooting the flashlight around the various corners of the queer little sloping attic, "is be careful to walk only on those rafters. Be careful not to step on that plaster there, because it's flimsy. That's the ceiling of the room below, see?"

"I can easily straddle those scantlings," I said. "How do we lay the stuff?"

"It comes in chunks," said Jim, "each one exactly fits between the scantlings. You just lay them in, slightly overlapping."

"All right," I said, rubbing my hands. "Get down and pass me up the bags. It shouldn't take half an hour."

"You see," inquired Jim, "that there is hardly room for me up here?"

"Did it ever occur to you," I retorted, "what a handicap size is?"

Jim dropped down through the trap-door and I adjusted the flashlight to throw a beam that would light the whole chamber. Then Jim passed up the big bags, which were light as pillows and I tossed the ten of them variously around where they would be handiest.

"Do you need slippers?" asked Jim, sticking his head up through the trap-door to watch the proceedings. "Or running shoes?"

"I'm a cat on my feet," I assured him, tearing off the top of the first bag.

Like a Sailor in the Rigging

Out came square chunks of white fluff. I squatted down, my feet braced on the scantlings, and backed up, frog fashion, laying the squares in the space between the scantlings as I backed. In two minutes, I had completed one whole row.

"Puh," I laughed, "twelve dollars! Why, it won't take 20 minutes to do this job. Time me, Jim."

Jim looked at his watch.

"Seven-forty," he said. "Let's say we started at 7.35."

"Okay," I said, skipping cleverly along the rafters like a deep-sea sailor in the rigging of a ship, and ripping open a fresh bag.

The space was restricted, and I could not quite stand upright, and a slight ache in the back began to be noticeable; but that is my age, not my size. I squatted down and backed up, rapidly laying the squares of fluff and tamping the edges to overlap slightly.

"Seven-forty-three," times Jim, as I reached the end of the second row.

I nipped back along the scantlings, snatched up a fresh bag and started to tip the top open. As I partly straightened to get a good grip at the paper bag, my head came heavily and violently against one of the rafters above. I was unbalanced.

"Hoy," bellowed Jim.

But in attempting to regain my balance, one foot wave in the air and came heavily down, not on the scantling but on the plaster in between.

"Ooooooh," bellowed Jim in a high, anguished voice.

I felt my foot go through with a sickening sound of splintering and crackling. To rescue that foot, I tried to gain a better hold with the other. It, too, found no security, but, with a rending and crackling sound, like tramping on a fruit basket, went lightly and dizzily into nether space. I fetched up solidly astride a scantling, my feet hanging.

Jim had disappeared from the trap door. I heard him bellowing and moaning below.

"Jim," I shouted, "come and get me out of this."

He came and stuck his head up.

"Hoist yourself," he said, hoarsely.

"My pant legs," I explained, "are caught by the laths."

"Work yourself up," he suggested bitterly.

I struggled. But my pants were snagged securely by the broken ends of laths.

"Slip your pants off," said Jim, "and I'll catch them from below."

So I wormed myself out of my pants and Jim tossed them back up the trap-door to me, only a little dusty.

"I'm awfully sorry, Jim," I said to him, looking down. "Will we postpone it, for a while?"

"Heat," muttered Jim. "Heat. Heat has done this."

"I guess it would be better to get an expert to do this sort of thing," I suggested, as I came down the step-ladder.

"I guess so," said Jim, leading me in to see the pretty bedroom all ruined looking now.

"Oooofff," we both said as the car door opened. Mr. Jackson was sitting, feet up, with Lightning beside him and the skunk wrapped in a red handkerchief on the seat.

Skunked Again

"WHAT I like about the country," declared Jimmie Frise, "is the people."

"All the scallywags," I explained, "have been chased out of the country and have gone and hidden in the cities."

"Well," said Jim, "that may be a little broad. But it covers the situation. For instance, a young man grows up on the farm and turns out to be a little too bright for the country."

"It's the same thing," I defined. "What does too bright usually mean?"

"Thousands of the finest people in cities," stated Jim, "have come from the farms."

"And thousands of the cities' worst rascals, too," I insisted. "Let's be fair."

"At any rate," argued Jim, as we drove eagerly out into the wintry farm country, "we are agreed on one thing — there is a process of selection going on, as between city and country, that is leaving a mighty decent lot of pleasant gentle people in the country. They are not the ambitious type. Not the grasping and grafting type."

"Gumption is the word," I interrupted. "If anybody has any gumption, they pack up and go to the city. And gumption covers a multitude of qualities, from the kind a young fellow has who becomes one of our greatest surgeons or ministers, to the kind of fellow who wants to skin widows and orphans alive."

"Well," explained Jim, "a man couldn't become a great surgeon living on a lonely farm. You've got to give a man a terrible lot of sick and diseased people, before he can become a great physician. And as for widows and orphans, they are few and far between , in the country, with plenty of people watching them all the time. A fellow couldn't work up a real business skinning widows and orphans out here."

"It's curious," I remarked, "that there is really no counter-flow of people from the cities."

"It's on account of the plumbing, pure and simple," said Jim. "Once accustom people to hot and cold water and indoor plumbing generally, and you can never get them back to the out-side pump. There are in cities, tens of thousands, yes, perhaps millions of people who are living in misery and degradation, jobless, homeless, who would be happy as kings living on farms, working the slow, patient life, amidst the cattle and the land. But they prefer to live in degradation, with hot and cold laid on, rather than risk having to dig a path in the snow."

"Some day," I predicted, "cities will have walls again. So many are becoming dependant in cities, that taxes will presently be unable to bear the strain. Then the cities will build walls around themselves. And to get inside, you'll have to have a passport, identifying you either as a citizen or as a business man on business bent. For every country man wanting to move in, arrangements will have to be made for a city man to move out. Suppose a bright young man on the farm has the makings of a distinguished banker. Before he can get into a city he will have to arrange with his parents or relatives or the county council to ac-cept a young city man to come and live in the country."

Looking for Jack-rabbits

"It sounds Chinese," said Jim.

"I shouldn't wonder," I admitted. "The Chinese figured these things out thousands of years ago. Then they let the white man in, and now look at China. There is something essentially silly about white men, don't you think?"

"I often get that notion," agreed Jim, "hearing them talk."

"Sooner or later," I declared, "the country has got to cease producing bright young men."

"Of course," suggested Jim, "we're forgetting that there is a certain flow of city men back into the country. I mean the retired bankers and big shots who buy swell big farms."

"A lovely trade that is." I agreed. "Imagine a pleasant comfortable township having a big shot suddenly come and buy 400 acres. A big shot used to having his own way and wangling everything he wanted by the methods familiar to all big shots."

"Well," said Jim, "the reeve and council and the various committees and the church warden and managers, in that case, will appreciate the feelings of city men when some son of the soil rises in their midst and becomes general manager."

"Fortunately," I pointed out, "these city big shots only come out to the country in their old age. It isn't for long. Their children never dream of keeping the farm on. It comes back, after a little while, into the kindly arms of the country once more."

"At a nice bargain," said Jim.

"Where," I inquired, looking out over the wintry fields heaving away to the frosty skyline, "were you figuring we'd start looking for jack-rabbits."

"It's only three or four concessions up," said Jim, giving the car the gas. "I was talking to some kids that were on their way home from school, and they said nobody ever hunts around here. And I saw jack-rabbits in about one mile."

So we sat and watched the country wheel by, the huddled little farm homes, lost amidst the wide barren fields which, in summer, they seem to dominate. How curious it is that in summer a farmhouse seems to own its landscape. And in winter, the same farmhouse seems to own nothing.

As we rolled, we kept a wary eye for the big brown hares which in Ontario go by the mistaken name of jack-rabbits. They are the true European hare, a great big foreign hare that stays brown all year round, and goes to 12 and 15 pounds in weight commonly, and three or four pounds greater than that on occasion. It was introduced, as far as anybody can discover, during the war, when a breeder of them, down near Brantford, had a large pen of them washed away in a flood. From that 50 or so hares, they have multiplied to hundred of thousands and have spread all over central Ontario and provide game for hunters by the tens of thousands. There are 80,000 gun licenses sold in Ontario, and about 50,000 of that number generally point at a jack-rabbit, so called, at least a few times in November and December. Jim's and mine are two of them.

"This," said Jim, as we came over a rise, "looks like the spot."

Fence-Climbing and Clod-Hopping

Fields of stubble, fields of plow and green patches of winter wheat lifting away for rolling miles looked like the terrain favored by the big jacks. We saw some patches where the hares had scratched the frosty earth around the winter wheat. Parking the car on the ditch shoulder, we dismounted, set up guns and started for the pleasant game of fence-climbing and clod-hopping which is jack hunting. Separating the width of a field, and moving slowly and watchfully for the sudden springing and skedaddling big hares, we did four fences when we spied, coming towards us, a burly big figure of a man with a gun over his arm and a hound forlornly beside him. Jim crossed the field to me.

"Here's somebody," said Jim, "can tell us where the jacks are. Whenever you see a man with a hound in the country, you know he isn't feeding a hound for nothing. A hound is a one-purpose job. It won't fetch cattle. It won't guard the house, being away hunting most of the time. See a hound, in the country, and you've got a man with an eye to rabbits, foxes, and coons."

We went forward and met the stranger.

"Howdy," he called cheerfully. "A nice day for scent, and not a rabbit in the county."

We all leaned our guns up against the fence in the approved country fashion and prepared for a little conversation.

"I came past here a month ago," said Jim, "and saw three jacks in the fields just as I passed by. I thought this particular stretch would be crawling with them."

"Them there," said the stranger, "must have been the three I got at the start of the season, me and Lightning here. If there is a rabbit in the township, Lightning will find him and tell the whole world, day and night, day after day, until somebody comes and shoots it to keep him quiet. All I do is keep coming out to shut

Lightning up. The township protests about him all the time, so I got to keep coming out and shoot rabbits."

"They must be kind of scarce around here, then?" Jim asked.

"A rabbit," said the stranger, whose name was Mr. Jackson, "is very ill-informed to come into this township. But I know a spot about seven miles north of here. Man, oh man."

"Seven miles is nothing," said Jim. "In a car."

"Ah, yes," said Mr. Jackson, sadly, "but a car is exactly what I haven't got. Perhaps it's a blessing or there wouldn't be any game in the whole County."

"Listen," said Jim, "we'd be only too delighted to have somebody show us where the shooting is, if you can spare the time. Our car is only out at the road there."

"Time?" said Mr. Jackson. "What is time?"

"Let's go," said Jim and I together.

And with the guns and hound eagerly sensing sport, we walked rapidly back out the road and got in the car, Mr. Jackson easing himself luxuriously in the back seat with Lightning.

"Straight ahead, until I tell you the turn," said Mr. Jackson.

It was a trifle more than seven miles, as a matter of fact. But country people have only a vague idea of distance. It was thirteen miles, and about eleven of it over pretty tough side roads that got wilder and more rocky and cedar swampy with every mile.

"This looks more like snowshoe rabbit country than jacks," said Jim, as we cautiously negotiated one of the several narrow steep inclines on a road that got swampier and more cedary.

"Them jacks," said Mr. Jackson, "are everywhere."

And guiding us left and right and north and west, we came at last to our destination, which was an abandoned farm with cedar swamps encroaching close about its crooked fields, an orchard lifting forsaken arms, and the rest of its scattered patches of brush stealing back, the advance guard of the eternal and ever-conquering wilderness that will haunt mankind to the utter end.

"Where do we hunt here?" I inquired a little doubtfully, for I like my jacks jumping neat out of stubble, at about 20 yards.

"I tell you, boys," said Mr. Jackson eagerly, "I'll just head into that cedar swamp with Lightning, and you two spread out and scuffle them meadows good. It's full of jacks. One day last winter, I got ten jacks in an afternoon, right here. Between here and the next cross roads."

"Won't you come with us?" Jim inquired. "There'll be no shooting down there unless it's white snowshoe rabbits."

"No, no," insisted Mr. Jackson. "It's jacks you're after. Go get 'em. Lightning and I will amuse outselves down there. I'm not as handy on my legs as I used to be."

So Jim and I scuffled off into the fields, and scuffle it was. Weeds and burrs, thickets of alder and willow, swampy patches rough and frozen into nasty nubbles, and not a sign of a jack by the time we got to the farthest end of the clearing and came to a bush.

In all the hundred acres, no life stirred, no chickadee, no squirrel. In these old abandoned farms there is a hush that both scares and heals, Jimmie and I stood by the remains of the rail fence, now fallen and already returning to the reaching earth, and harked. Men had come here, and destroyed the hard covering that had succeeded in taking hold on this thin soil, over these rocks. But none of man's delicate creations had roots enough to take hold in their turn. Now, after many years, the harsh advance agents of nature, the weeds, the briars, the willows, were slowly getting their grip into it again. The men and women who had come here lived in hope and pride. They left only a scar. And even the little winter birds could find nothing to eat in it.

"It's kind of eerie," murmured Jim.

"All the big companies," I replied bravely to scare away the ghosts, "all the big corporations, all the great churches, halls, all the long handsome streets, will be like this some day."

"This time of year," said Jim, "it gets gray and gloomy early in the afternoon."

"Little or big," I declared, "it all works out the same in the end. Men come in, so proud and loaded with seed..."

"We'll head up the road," said Jim. "There will be more farms beyond."

We heard Lightning suddenly begin baying, and almost immediately the sound of a shot.

"The old boy," said Jim, "is getting swamp hare. What do you say we go back and have a day at the white bunnies?"

"Aw," I said, "my children won't speak to me for several days after I bring home a white hare. Let's go after the big boys."

And we had got half a mile up the road, seeing nothing but rough clearings and no open fields in sight, when we heard a car horn blowing steadily, in long signals.

"That sounds like my horn," said Jim.

"Maybe the old boy has struck good hunting," I said. "Let's go back."

So we retraced our steps down the rutted frozen swamp road and came to the car, where Mr. Jackson was sitting, feet up, and pipe going, with Lightning in beside him.

"Mmmfff, mfff, mfff," said Jim, as we neared the car.

"Oooooffff," we both said, as the car door opened.

Couldn't Breathe in a City

"I got him," said Mr. Jackson, comfortably, patting an old red handkerchief on the seat beside him. "Lightning and me."

"So it seems," said Jim, standing back. "A skunk?"

"We first spotted him," said Mr. Jackson excitedly, "three weeks ago, in this very swamp. But he got into a stone pile. Neither of us has had our proper rest since, worrying about this skunk. One dollar that skin's worth."

Mr. Jackson patted the red handkerchief, which bundled something flabby and terrible within.

"One dollar?" said Jim, breathing out.

"Common skins," said Mr. Jackson, "are worth 60 cents. But this here one, it's the biggest I see in years, and beautifully marked. Wait till I show you."

"No, no," cried Jim. "Let it lay."

Jim looked at me and I at Jim, in one of those instantaneous glances that make plans and settle questions without a word being said. We got in. We drove Mr. Jackson home, back all the winding, steep back roads, while he sat comfortably in rear, chatting pleasantly, and fondling Lightning, who whoofed deliciously from time to time.

"Tell me, Mr. Jackson," I inquired, in the midst of his reminiscences, "are you a native of this part of the province?"

"No, sir," said Mr. Jackson sitting forward happily, "I'm not. You wouldn't take me for a city-bred man, now, would you?"

"There is something about you..." I said, turning to look at him and also to lean a little farther away.

"Well, sir", said he, expansively. "I was born and raised in the city but I couldn't stick it. I can't go cities or towns. I feel as if I couldn't breathe in a city. So I up and left it as a young man. I shook the dust of cities off my feet as soon as I was old enough to be my own boss."

We drove Mr. Jackson right to his door, and a little old shanty

it was.

"Not much to look at," he said heartily, as he and Lightning got out with their package, "But it's all I ask."

He thanked us profusely, regretting we had seen no jacks on such a lucky day at that.

"And by the way," he said, as he slammed the door and stepped up to shake hands through the front windows, "if you notice any little smell of skunk in the car, though I don't notice it myself, just use vinegar. A quart of raw vinegar, slosh it around. It'll kill the slightest trace of it."

"Thank YOU," we assured him.

"Thank YOU," he corrected, as we geared away.

"It's getting a little late," I informed Jim.

"Well," said Jim, "we always seem to get something when we go hunting."

"Let's stop," I suggested, "at the next corner and get a quart of vinegar."

"*While a blizzard howled around the cottage, Jim crouched by the fire, while I crept under a mattress and picked my shoes from a snow bank on the floor.*

Up Where the North Begins

"**D**O you realize," said Jimmie Frise, more to make conversation than anything "that right now, in the dead of winter, there are more than 40 different kind of birds living right around us here in Ontario?"

"Song birds?" I inquired.

"Yes, song birds," stated Jim, "although they aren't singing just now."

"The silly things," I said.

"Ah, they're quite happy," said Jim. "You see, a bird's normal temperature is over 130 degrees. They don't feel the cold the way we do."

"The silly things," I repeated. "When they've got the means to go south. When all they've got to do is up and fly away, and in about a week's easy going, be in Mexico or Yucatan."

"Well, you see," explained Jim, "these are northern birds. They nest up in the Arctic. They think this is real balmy to-day. They've come a thousand miles south already. They think this is down south."

"Huh," said I.

"It's all a matter," elucidated Jim, "of relativity. The birds that nest here go south. The birds that nest in the Arctic come down here."

"And the ones that nest in the south?" I inquired.

"They go right into the tropics," said Jim. "Birds are very discontented."

"Discontented?" I scoffed. "You mean smart. They grew wings. And what did we grow? Just legs. Fat, slow, lumbering legs. And where can we go on legs?"

"Ah, but we grew brains," pointed out Jim.

"Well," I maintained, "a bird has brains too. All it needs. And when a bird thinks, with its little brain, that it wants to go to Mexico, all it does is get up and fly there. But when we, with our big, fat brains, think we want to go to Mexico, what do we do? Can we get up and go there? No, sir. We can just sit here and think about it. I think humans are saps, if you want to know."

"We stay here," argued Jim, "because we've got the ability to build houses and be warm. A bird can't protect itself against the winter, so it has to leave."

"Still, the more I think of it," I insisted, "the more I think humans are saps. If instead of wasting time learning how to build houses we had grown wings, we'd have been better off in the end. Now that we have chosen to remain in one place and dig ourselves in, what good does it do us? Are we any better off, sitting here like slugs in a cave, than if we were skittering hither and yon? I mean, use your common sense, Jimmie. Who decided for us that we would be better off stuck down in one spot, the way we are? That's that I want to know. Who chose for us all this living and dying in one spot, like a lot of cabbages?"

"Good heavens," said Jim, "you can't rebel against human nature."

"As a matter of fact," said he, "it takes a long time to alter human nature or any kind of nature. It takes ages of time and countless generations. One thing is sure, we two can't change.

Each of us is like a coin stamped out in a mint. All that ever happens to us is that we grow a little worn and faded. But the imprint stays on us to the end."

"It's cruel," I said.

"And the comical part of it is," went on Jim, "that for countless ages to come, there will be guys exactly like us, thinking the same silly things, yearning and dreaming, but never changing a whit."

"It's dreadful," I muttered. "I'd like to meet up with those birds, about two million years ago, who decided to be us."

"There is only one thing to do," said Jim, a little importantly. "And that is, make the best of it. Instead of running away from life, attack it. Instead of cringing from cold and dark and fear, stand up and walk right into it."

"Ah," said I. "Hero stuff."

"Not at all," said Jim. "Life in the end is just one slow, steady defeat. Nobody ever wins. We lose our strength. We see all our works crumble. Our friends fall away. We die. We can't possibly escape, so why run? Why always be cringing and whimpering and running like hell?"

"Who's running?" I demanded.

"Why," cried Jim, "you were even wanting to fly."

"I was merely wanting," I stated with dignity, "to be comfortable."

"Comfort," stated Jim, "is relative. Here we are sitting in a comfortable house, slouched down in a couple of easy chairs, with soft music coming from Los Angeles, across five thousand miles of blizzard, and there isn't a thing we want, from a drink of water to a heated sixty-mile-an-hour vehicle out in our heated garage, that we can't have. On a night of storm and tempest, here we are snug as a couple of bugs in a buffalo rug. Yet in five minutes, without the slighest effort, we can be in a beautiful theatre looking at the greatest actors and most beautiful actresses culled from America, England, Germany, Sweden. Or, in ten minutes, we can be sitting at a silver cluttered table, in a swell cafe, eating chicken sandwiches made by a French chef."

"Mmmm," said I, sitting up.

To Escape From Comfort

"Yet," said Jim, "I am willing to bet you that there are men, at this very hour lying in a little silk tent in a deep excavation in the snow, a thousand miles north of us, with their husky dogs snuggled around and a fire burning gaily, and those men, miles from any human habitation, lost in a wild blizzard raging, are more comfortable than we are."

"What will they be eating?" I inquired.

"Bacon," said Jim, "and flapjacks smothered in maple syrup."

"Mmmm," I repeated, sitting up higher and scratching my head.

"You see?" said Jim. "The less comfort you have, the more you enjoy comfort. The trouble with us is, we never escape from comfort. To really enjoy life, we ought to expose ourselves to discomfort a little more than we do. We ought to take up skiing, or go for long tramps in the open. We ought to suffer our climate occasionally, so as to appreciate how cleverly we have skunked it."

"To tell the truth, Jim," I confessed, "I've often looked at those pictures of winter camping in the outdoor magazines with a curious impulse. I've darn near gone on winter camping trips."

"Darn near isn't near enough," retorted Jim.

"Many's the time," I assured him, "I've thought of having a winter house party up at our cottage."

And Jim, with a joyous glitter in his eye, slowly rose from amongst the cushions of the big chair, and looked at me with open mouth. And that is how it came about.

Our first idea, then and there talked out and elaborated for a lovely and enthusiastic hour, was to take all our families. We even got to the list of provisions. We even telephoned long distance for forty cents to the postmaster at the little village, seven miles from the summer resort, to ask how the roads were at this time of year. And he told us they were swell. Plowed every day.

But our families were all tied up. Jim's had skiing party engagements and Sunday teas; mine had all promised themselves in various ways for at least three week-ends to come.

But those lists of provisions fairly burned in our pockets. And when Jimmie took me up to his attic closet and emptied out old dunnage bags full of mackinaw coats and hunting pants and oil-tanned moccasins that hadn't been used for fifteen years, the family side of the enterprise began to fade anyway.

"They'd turn it," said Jim, "into a taffy-pulling, dish-washing, community-singing sort of thing. We'll make it stag. We'll just go up and spend the week-end tramping over the hills and visiting the settlers in their snowed-in cabins. Will they be surprised?''

"And," I said, '' we can take along our guns in case we jump a cottontail.''

"And," contributed Jim, "I'll bring along that Bird Guide of mine and we can identify some winter birds.''

"Swell," I agreed.

A White Vastness

Really, the drive up was beautiful. The highways are kept scraped as clean as the pavement. The vast white country, miles and miles, is utterly new, despite all the years we have passed through it in summer. A thousand interesting and old-fashioned interests attract the eye, the farmers in sleighs, the villages and towns so steamy and quaint-looking under their mantles of white. Except for Jim's anti-freeze having got thin and a little boil-up we had south of Severn Bridge, we made as good time as we do in July. But the engine boiling halted us a good hour on the road, and then we had to go by easy stages until we got to a garage, and in all a couple of hours were lost. But even the visits to garages were interesting, in winter. Everybody up north has a different air, in the off season.

At last we reached the gravel road that goes east towards "the Lake", as we call it, and here the plowing was not so governmental as on the highways. In fact, we slowed down to about 15. I think all those country drivers you see bumbling along at 15 in summer practise most of their driving in winter.

It was dusk when we passed through the village, the last outpost of civilization. We stopped in to see the postmaster and storekeeper and had a jovial chat. It was dark when we started the last seven miles in to the cottage. But the headlights threw a glorious beam on the fantastic and wholly unfamiliar scenery of the road we knew in summer. And when we reached the lane that leads down to the lake, by the cottage, the snow-clad boards pointed down two deep ruts between enormous lake-blown drifts, and we knew we could take the car no farther.

Shouldering our packs and provision boxes we left the car at the corner and walked down the ruts. Under the stars, a white vastness stretched afar where in summer the dark lake lay. With merry shouts and scrunching feet and not a little leaving of boxes of provisions to be come back for later, we followed the ruts past the last settler's house, its lights glimmering in the distance, and waded through drifts along the abandoned road, past strange, shuttered cottages of neighbors, utterly foreign now; and came, with a feeling of Commander Peary, to our own cottage, memorable despite the masses of snow, crouched amidst its tapering firs.

We unlocked the door. It was bitter. I lit a match and fumbled up at the iron switch box that turns on the power. It clicked. But no light came.

"H'm," I remembered. "They cut off the power into here at the end of the season."

"There'll be lamps?" said Jim.

With matches, I hunted lamps in remote back shelves of closets. But careful housewives had emptied lamps.

"Get the fire on the hearth," I cried cheerily, "while I find the coal oil."

So Jim, with matches, went out and scratched up kindling at the woodpile against the house and I went seeking. All the tins rang hollow. In vain, I searched drawers for candles, looked along the mantel for colored candles in silly summer candlesticks. There were none. Jim was kneeling at the stone fireplace, and faint flames fluttered uncertainly.

"The kindling is wet," he said. "Frozen. You never should pile wood against the house, on account of the autumn drip. It soaks it."

"Get her going," I said. "This house is like a tomb. It's colder than outside."

Jim struggled and burned leaping flares of newspaper, and piled and repiled the kindling: but got no fire.

"Here," I said, "you go and pick up those boxes of provisions we left and at the same time drop in at the settler's, it's only a couple of hundred yards beyond, and borrow a bottle of coal oil. I'll show you a fire."

A Losing Battle

So Jim went out into the starry night and I got to work on the fire. But it was true. A woodpile that does fine against the house in hot summer is no good for winter. All the wood was frozen. I went out and floundered about breaking twigs off trees. I got a little fire going, but the larger wood refused to take hold. I went out and tore down the woodpile to get at some of the under stick. But autumn's drip had saturated them all. Jim was a long time coming home.

In the intervals of making the fire blaze a little, I pulled cots out of the adjoining rooms and set them in front of the fireplace. I put the dunnage bags on them. Spread out some of my stuff.

I heard Jim coming in. At the moment, the fire happened to be just failing for the tenth time.

"I called at the settler's," said Jim, "but there was nobody home but a big black dog who wouldn't let me look around the woodshed or anything."

So we went out and floundered in the drifts and collected two or three large armfuls of twigs and what we hoped were dead branches, and I found a couple of pieces of loose board on the back veranda, and we got enough fire going to light the room enough to spread out our blankets. But the chunks of maple we leaned up so invitingly in the blaze would not take fire. They hissed. They sizzled. But they would not take fire.

"Let's go into bed," said Jim, "while we have enough light to see."

Which we did. And it was good, with all our clothes on, to snuggle down amongst the blankets and lie watching the little fire fight and struggle and snap and crackle in its valiant battle for existence. But even as we drowsed, we knew it was a losing battle.

In the night, a moaning waked us, and on the window, we could hear the sound of snow. The room was dark, the fire was dead.

"Blizzard," said Jim, heavily.

As host, I went into the adjoining room and brought out a couple of mattresses to lay on top of us.

In the morning, gray and terrible, the window was snowed up and a drift had blown in unseen cracks. The floor was inches deep in places and our boots lifted pathetic mouths up out of it, as though gasping. Jim crouched out of bed and hastily burned some more newspapers.

"We can go out," he said, "and find some wood now. We'll be eating in half an hour."

"Jim," I said, emptying my boot, "how about eating at that Chinese restaurant we had supper in last night?"

"That's 30 miles," stated Jim.

"Even so," I suggested.

So we got dressed stiffly and packed up our stuff and carried it out to the car, which was all but drifted under, and, it being Sunday, no snow-plow came by this early, so it was a long, anxious drive the seven miles out to the postmaster's, where we had breakfast and bought a shovel and waited until the snow-plow came by, and enjoyed a long, pleasant conversation about the old pioneer days with plenty of extra cups of coffee.

*"What's the matter?" I asked.
"You've got the wrong tickets!"
said the girl ...*

Scalped in the Rush

"**I**T'S ages," said Jimmie Frise, "since we've been to a pro. hockey game."

"Let's go," I agreed promptly. "There's a big game to-night."

"Yeah," said Jim, "you're like everybody else. You never attend any games until the last minute, and then you expect to get seats just by driving down and walking in the door."

"Listen, big boy," I informed him, "you're not on to the ropes of this sport business. There are always scalpers."

142

"Yes, ten bucks for a $1.65 seat," said Jim.

"Heh, heh," I laughed heartily, "naturally you'd pay ten bucks if you went down scrounging around about 8 o'clock. But old dogs like me, we know the tricks. We don't even start to look for a scalper until 8.30, just after the game starts. Then the scalper is to anxious, he sells for three or even two bucks, to get his money out of it. See?"

"It's an idea," admitted Jim, admiringly. "How did you catch on to all this sport racket? I thought you had no use for the sit-down sports."

"Really," I confided, "I haven't any use for the sit-down sports. Any sport that involves 12 men playing and 12,000 sitting on their beam ends looking, isn't a sport by any stretch of the imagination. It's an entertainment, but not a sport. The only sport about it involves the dozen players."

"I know lots of people," stated Jim, "that get far more excitement, action and exercise sitting watching a hockey game than they'd get if they were playing."

"It isn't a sport," I insisted. "Even if they get hysterics, it still isn't a sport. It's only a nervous reaction. Sport is too loosely used a word, these last 50 years. Sport is hunting, fishing, riding to hounds, playing games, such as tennis, football or hockey. But sitting like a lot of dopes watching, doesn't admit you into the sacred precincts of sport. Yet there are thousands and thousands of people going brightly and eagerly through life, rushing to grandstands and sitting furiously on the seats of their pants, cuddling in their silly minds the notion that they too belong to the sport world."

"Well, weren't we contemplating going to to-night's game?" inquired Jim.

"Those people," I declared hotly; "are as far from sport as the people sitting in movie theatre are from being movie stars."

"How about to-night?" insisted Jimmie.

"They're just an audience, that's all," I concluded.

"O.K.," agreed Jim, "but how about us going to to-night's game? How about us sitting furiously on the seats of our pants for a couple of hours tonight?"

"I'm with you," I said enthusiastically. "It's time we stirred up our sluggish corpuscles with a glimpse of sport's most glorious spectacle."

"You said it," admitted Jim.

"I didn't say half of it," I protested, "If you think that is all hockey is, my friend, you are much mistaken. Hockey, I say it with moderation and after carefully weighing my words, is without question the fastest, gayest, most violent and at the same time most graceful sport spectacle the world has yet seen. Maybe some day, in the long years to come, they can work out some game played with teams of aeroplanes at five miles a minute against the heavenly blue. But until then, hockey is the greatest sport spectacle ever invented.''

"You said it," repeated Jim.

"My dear sir," I said heatedly, "I haven't half said it. Hockey is so far ahead of...''

"It's the asparagus," I apologized. "New asparagus always makes me nippy like this. But as I was saying, Jim, hockey is so far ahead of all other sports, it is a great wonder to me all the other sports haven't died years ago, out of sheer comparison. Football is all right,because it has the essential element of shock, of collision. But it is slow, like a herd of buffalo stampeding across the distant scene. Whereas hockey has all the shock and collision, but it is like greased lighning, and it's right under your eye.''

"Ah," breathed Jim, "the greenish-gray ice, the hawk-like figures weaving patterns.''

"Horse-racing has speed," I went on, "but it is all over in two minutes. And most of it, except the finish, is just a dull muddle.''

"Of course," objected Jim, "you never did see horse-racing. But wait till you make your first two-dollar bet.''

"Bet?" I scoffed. "What has betting got to do with sport?''

"Well, it's like this," said Jim. "Suppose you bet me $5 Maple Leafs will win to-night and I bet you $5 that Maroons will win?''

"I'd take it in a minute," I informed him, "if it wasn't like taking money from a baby.''

"Oh, is that so?" said Jim. "Well, if you are so free with $5 bills, come right in.''

"No, Jim," I explained, "it wouldn't increase my enjoyment of the game to-night. It would spoil it. I would keep thinking, all through the game, of the $5 you can ill-afford to lose, and which I was about to take from you.''

"Look here," cried Jim, " you don't even begin to understand the function of wagering. It is to put a kick into contests. If you are so darn cocksure about the Maple Leafs to-night...''

"That is why I can't bet," I explained patiently. "Just

"Box seats," stated the stranger.
"Two-fifty, the same as I paid."

because I am so cocksure. If I wasn't so sure, it might be fun to have a little bet with you. Then I would have personal reasons, petty though they might be, to help me enjoy the game, to give it a false zest. Like putting Worcestershire sauce on a hotel steak."

"Will you listen to me for just one minute?" asked Jim rather quietly. "Sort of halt your mind, please. Just bring everything to a standstill. Sort of let your mind go limp, to see if you can possibly take in what I am going to say."

"Go ahead," I said, trying to relax.

"I tell you," said Jim, slowly, "that the Maple Leafs have all gone to pot. That they are just a shadow of a once noble team. That they haven't got one good hockey player in the team. They haven't even got a decent skater."

"The Maple Leafs, you mean?" I said concentrating. "The Toronto Maple Leafs?"

"Yes," said Jim, tensely, "Them. I tell you they have got about as much chance of beating Montreal tonight as you have of knocking out Joe Louis."

"Jim," I said, "you wouldn't be joking or anything?"

"I tell you the Maple Leafs are a palooka team," rasped Jim.

"In that case," I said, "I think I might take you for $5 on them. Or, say, make it two."

"No, $5," said Jim, firmly, "I'd sooner make it $10."

"No, $5," I agreed. "I haven't followed hockey much this year except on the radio for the middle period when usually somebody or other comes in and then I forget by Monday to look at who won. But it seems to me, from what little I've heard, that the Maple Leafs..."

"Ah, hedging," sneered Jim.

"Hedge nothing," said I smartly. "And if they are as bad as you say, it behooves all good Torontonians to get in there and cheer their team to victory. I will, for one."

"You will," agreed Jim. "Now."

So we agreed to leave at 8 p.m., which would get us down in time to park and arrive just about 8.30,when the scalpers would be getting anxious.

"Scalpers, you see, Jim," I explained, as we started off, "are illegal. They can't come out in the open. They have to work very furtively, because there are not only cops watching, but lots of employees, who, if they detect a scalper, will quietly tip off a detective, and the jig's up."

"Isn't it illegal then," asked Jim, "to buy from a scalper?"

"No," I informed him, "It is never illegal for the rich to buy. It is only illegal for the poor to sell."

"How do the scalpers get their tickets?" asked Jim. "The box office won't sell big bunches of tickets."

"No," I elucidated, "the scalper gets a dozen of his bum friends to get in line and buy him up 24 seats at say $1.65. Then when the big crowd gathers, he mooches in amongst them, sizing up his prospects carefully, and offers them at a price he thinks he can get. Especially young fellows with girls. Especially young fellows that look as if they were in love."

"It might be a good racket," agreed Jim, "if you were a good judge of human nature."

So when we got down and parked in one of the lots where there is always miraculously room for just one more car, we strolled along in the hustling thrusting, rude play-off crowds, taking our time as if we were the holders of box seats in the centre section.

"We'll take our time," I explained, "Let the crowd thin out. Probably by this time, we have been the subject of speculative gaze of a dozen scalpers. But they're still up in the five-dollar plane."

We walked along, getting at last into the mob and being lock-stepped slowly and stuffily towards the entrance. We got inside and stood in the densely locked mob there, the mob that I never could figure out what they were doing. They weren't waiting for anybody, obviously, because nobody could find anybody in there. I think they are just the crowd lovers. There are dog lovers, horse lovers, book lovers, stamp collector and crowd lovers. They just get a kind of queer thrill by standing stupidly , with a faraway expression, in a dense mob.

So we stood for a few minutes doing that too, and by the far thunder of cheers muffled through the doors, we knew the game was starting and the stampede of the late-comers began, the flush-faced, breathless pushing and shoving and running flat-footed up concrete stairs.

"Well, Jim," I said, quietly, "I guess we can step outside now and take a stroll around."

"I didn't see anybody giving me the eye," said Jim.

"Not in here, no," I said out of the side of my mouth. "Didn't you notice the dicks standing amidst that crowd?"

We got through the doors, past colliding incomers with a wild

*"We slowly retreated, glancing
backward all the way."*

148

expression in their eyes when they heard that far thunder of the herd within. In the street, there were both hurrying and loitering figures.

"Walk along," I hissed, "in an anxious way, and look everybody you meet in the eye."

But Not Cheering

We walked along, bent forward, and peering at everybody. But nobody but a young policeman met our anxious gaze. We got to the corner.

From the doorway at the corner, a slight, flat-chested figure stepped furtively towards us. I nudged Jim.

"Gents," asked the furtive one in a low voice, "could you use a couple of tickets for the game?"

"How much?" I said, tough.

"Two-fifty each," said the stranger, "I found out at the last minute I couldn't go."

"Two-fifty," I snorted, "what are they, standing room?"

"Box seats," stated the stranger, keeping his eye sharply right and left. "Box seats. Two-fifty apiece, the same as I paid."

He held out two bright red tickets.

Jim and I dug. We handed him the money and we turned and walked easily towards the entrance.

Jim started to laugh.

"You, " he laughed, "and your scalpers! And we come down here and pick up a couple of choice seats from some poor little decent fellow..."

"We just happen to be lucky," I protested. "Let's get a move on."

We joined a belated straggle and went through the turnstiles. Even the ticket-taker in the derby hat was excited. We went through the passage and gave our tickets to the girl in the blue cape and she was breathless and could hardly look at us, so furiously did the glorious game go.

Like a great gale of wind, the passion of the place blew over us. In no other game is there such mass concentration as in this hockey. Fifteen thousand people all focussed as one. Thirty thousand eyes glued on the one vital incident, for so harmonious are all the elements of light, of color, of space, that attention cannot relax. Attention is nailed. It is hypnotic.

"Get going" I muttered, as Jim slowed to lift on tip toe to see some play in close.

"Yaaarrh," roared Jimmie, in that unintelligible but noble

language of hockey.

With a mighty sound, the whole vast place rose to its feet and screamed, and the little girl in the cape beckoned us hastily.

She showed us to our seats and we trampled into them, our eyes rivetted on the game. The place was one vast song of valiant sound. We were still rivetted on the play, I cheering madly a Maple rush and Jim screaming raspingly a Maroon break-up of the rush, when, only a moment after we sat down we felt, rather than saw, the breathless girl in the usher's cap beckoning and nudging.

"What is it?" cried Jim.

"Your stubs please?" cried the girl thinly in the tumult. Jim fumbled for them and nudged me. I fumbled too. I found them.

The girl looked at them briefly and then beckoned us up. A lady and gentleman, standing beside her, glared at us as we stumbled into the aisle.

We followed the girl down into the bottom aisle.

"What's the matter?" I asked, in the din, momentarily diverting my attention from the game.

"Wrong series," said the girl, in my ear. "Four weeks ago."

"Which?" I said.

"You've got the wrong tickets. That game was four weeks ago," said the girl hurriedly, trying to pay attention to the play.

I tugged Jim's sleeve. He was hard to distract. He was up on tip toe, wildly chearing and gesticulating at a play far down the ice.

"Where do we sit," he said, turning hurriedly. "Make it snappy."

So I explained it to him.

We slowly retreated along the aisle and down the passage to the exit, glancing backward all the way.

But not cheering.

Outside, we inquired, in vain, if there were any seats left. Any fifty-dollar scats, even.

But there weren't any, of course.

So as we went out into the night, Jim said he thought we should call the bet off, because a bet, on a unseen game, like a bet on an unseen horse race, was nothing but a vulgarity.

Weak~Enders

"**H**ow's that annex coming," inquired Jimmie Frise jovially, "on your summer cottage?"

"The lumber is delivered," I informed him. "I had a letter from Percy to say he had received it by truck and then he scowed it up to the cottage."

"Percy?" asked Jim.

"Percy's the general factotum up at the Landing." I explained.

"I can't just quite see a guy named Percy," said Jim, "receiving a load of lumber and delivering it by scow."

"Oh, you can't go by names," I laughed. "Percy is six feet high and weighs close to 300 pounds. He is tough, rough and handsome. I never saw him with a clean shave in the 30 years I've known him at the Landing. He can lift a rowboat as easy as you or I used to be able to lift a canoe".

"Don't keep spinning round,"
said Jim. "Stand still and hold
your wrist." But it seemed to feel
better if I kept spinning round.

"Used to be able, huh?" muttered Jim a little coldly.

"Yes, I said used to be," I submitted. "Percy is one of those indispensable fellows that grows up in every summer resort. Sometimes their name is Elmer. Sometimes it is Sidney. Usually it is a very deceptive name such as those. But the man is generally the same. Friendly, honest, upright and could use an outboard engine for an egg-beater in one hand."

"I don't much like," stated Jim, "that reference of yours to the fact that we used to be able to lift a canoe."

"It's true, Jimmie," I said gently. "Why deceive yourself?"

"Look," said Jim, "the trouble with us and most people is that we dramatize ourselves. We dramatize ourselves as growing old and feeble. As the years go by, we slowly relinquish our grip on life. I tell you, a man is as good at 50 as he is at 20, and there isn't a lumber camp or a coal mine or a ship at sea that doesn't prove it over and over."

"Ah, yes," I pointed out, "but those old sailors and lumberjacks keep fit all the time. They work hard year in and year out..."

"Nonsense," cried Jim. "Nobody keeps less fit, nobody takes worse care of themselves than sailors and lumberjacks. They toil and labor all day and sleep at night in damp, smelly bunks, amidst bad air. They eat coarse greasy food and far too much of it. They get cold, they sweat, they freeze, they get wet, they are exposed to every harmful element. And when their job ends they go to town on a great big spree. Yet for sheer strength, and power, a lumberjack or sailor of 50 is as good, generally, as any 30-year-old."

"It's the open air life," I argued.

"To Remember You By"

"You take your friend Percy," continued Jim heatedly. "What has he got that we haven't got? He works hard during July and August maybe, during the tourist season. But the rest of the year he just loafs around his shanty, over-eating, getting fat. I know those summer resort fellows."

"Heh, heh," I chuckled. "I'd like to see you and Percy on the opposite ends of a bale of hay carrying it."

"I suppose," said Jim, "that Percy is going to build your annex?"

"Certainly," I admitted. "Percy builds everything on our lake. He not only builds everything, from cottages and wharves and boathouses down to lattice-work veranda ends and ornamental benches, but he puts in all our ice and he paints all our boats and mends all our engines. He transports us and all our luggage to and from. He's the caretaker and keeps all our cottage keys. He knows where all the fish are. And he's a pretty good amateur doctor, in case of sunburn or fish bones stuck in the throat."

"With four week-ends ahead of you before your family is ready to go to the cottage," suggested Jim, "I wonder you don't try your hand at a little building yourself."

"Building" I replied, " is one of the few things I never try."

"It's the simplest thing in the world," said Jim. "The art of-building is inherent in all men."

"My grandfather was a carpenter," I informed him, "but he seems to have worked too hard at at; he must have worn out the taste for it. Because somehow I feel completely unmoved at the thought of planks and saws and hammers and things."

"Think," cried Jim, "of that annex to your cottage. Years from now your children and your grand children, long after you are gone, will point to that annex and say, 'Grandad built that with his own hands.' "

"It's only a sort of back kitchen," I protested.

"Even so," begged Jim, "what other monuments are you leaving behind you? What trace are you leaving? These newspapers you write for will be dusty files, through which nobody will ever look. Five years after you're gone people will mention your name and say, what was he now? A radio comedian, wasn't he?"

"Never," I said sharply

"Or," said Jim, looking up, "was he some kind of a cartoonist?"

"Never," I shouted. "Jim, I don't think it is fair of you to talk about things like this. All men are very sensitive about their memories."

"What are you doing," demanded Jim, "to leave something for even your children to remember you by? Just a few photographs, which will get old-fashioned and dusty and their frames will get shabby and out they go."

"Stop, Jim," I commanded.

"Yah, you see?" cried Jimmie. "You are going to be sunk without a trace. No work of your hands will remain. At least, these big manufacturers are leaving big factories to stand, big and empty, as a memorial to them for years after they're gone. All over the country, along railway tracks and sidings in every town, you see those big, vast, empty and decayed factories, memorials to a once noble and industrious old gent."

"And who remembers them?" I demanded.

"Oh, their grandchildren and certain aged lawyers and some retired trust company officers," said Jim, "and if you look closely, through the dust on the train window, you can faintly make out the name of the mighty firm painted along the top of the brick wall of the factory."

An Old Hand At Building

"I don't like your attitude, Jim," I declared. "It makes all these big shots of today and all these big buildings and everything seem kind of pitiful."

"Sure they're pitiful," said Jim. "And you're pitiful, too, writing and talking and strutting through life, yet in a minute or a day or a year, poof, what is left?"

"I could have my portrait painted in oils" I suggested.

"What you need to do," stated Jim, "instead of leaving everything to Percy in this offhand fashion, is to go to work and build that annex. Build it strong and true. Build it sturdy and well. And 50 years from now people will say, I remember the man who built that annex. He was a great little fellow. And then they'll start remembering anecdotes about you."

"But it's only sort of back kitchen, Jim" I pleaded. "If it were a cottage now. Or a pagoda. Or a sun house in rustic beams out on the point. But a measly back kitchen."

"If you want my advice," said Jim, "I'd start with the back kitchen and get some practice. And then, maybe in the fall or possibly next spring, build a pagoda or a summer house out on the point. That's the trick. Build something prominent and lasting, so that people will have to remember you."

"I always did think a pagoda would look nice, out on the point by the cottage," I confessed.

"O.K., then," said Jim; "why not do it?"

"Did you ever do any building?" I demanded

"I'm an old hand at it." assured Jim. "I've built boathouses, shanties, shacks, henhouses, roothouses, lean-tos, loblollies, hoojackapivviers and shenanigans."

"In that case," I offered, " you would be glad to come up with me this week-end and give me a hand with my annex."

"Exactly," cried Jim, delightedly, leaping up, "that's what I've been driving at for the past ten minutes."

"My dear boy," I exclaimed, "why didn't you say so? We can have a swell week-end."

"Hammering," cried Jim. "Banging. Sawing. Chopping. Biffing."

In which merry spirit we made lists of what we needed. We needed nails, paint, a saw, a brace and bit.

"And a level," said Jim.

"Ten pounds of nails" I contributed.

"Pooh," said Jim, "ten pounds of nails is nothing. Make it 20 pounds four-inch, three and two."

"And a gallon of paint," I added, "shutter green."

"Make it two gallons," said Jim. "I like plenty of paint when I'm painting. And a hammer?"

"There's a hammer up there," I stated. "Two hammers, in fact. An old hammer and a new hammer. There are always two hammers at every summer cottage."

"I'll take the new hammer," said Jim.

And Saturday morning, when we drove into the Landing, to go the four miles up the lake, to the cottage, we saw Percy, and I was very ashamed. I had hoped he would be absent, up the lake at one of his countless preseason jobs. But no, there he was, large as life, and he walked right over to the car and saw the paint and nails and stuff in the car and looked very disappointed. In fact, he went quite cool towards us. His breezy warmth vanished.

"I'm taking some of the stuff up with me, Percy" I laughed, "and my friend and I are going to do a litte preliminary hammering and tinkering."

"That's swell," said Percy, showing his back teeth in a bleak grin. "I'm so busy right now I don't know whan I'd ever get at that annex of yours."

"Oh, in that case," I cried, "it will work out fine."

And Percy being too busy to tow us up with his motor boat, we had to row the four miles. But it was a fine morning and we enjoyed the row.

We found the cottage smelling of dead oak leaves, mice and last summer's air, as usual. We opened doors and took off shutters and found all the pots and pans we had forgotten to turn upside down. We found the stovepipe just as badly rusted and rotten as all the other years; but, as in all the other years, it still worked.

We got lunch and took off our coats and vests. Jim even took off his shirt.

"When I work," he stated, "I work."

We carried scantlings up from the ragged pile Percy had left on the point. We carried up the packages of nails, the paint, the saw, level, brace and bit and all. We laid them around handy.

"Now," said Jim, "the hammers."

I went in and looked in the usual place. But there was no hammer there. Back of the ice box, no hammers. On the railing in the living room, no hammer. On none of the window ledges, where we had nailed up the windows last fall, any hammer.

"Come on, come on," called Jimmie. "The old hammer will do."

"Come and help look, Jim," I commanded. "It will be staring us right in the face around here somewhere."

But it wasn't. And we looked on shelves and in closets, under boxes and between piled mattresses. We overturned rowboats and opened drawers of old warped dressers , in vain. We went out and kicked through piles of dead leaves. We looked down on the dock and up at the icehouse.

"There were two hammers here when I left last fall," I stated loudly. "Two hammers. An old one and a new one."

"All we need," said Jim, "is one."

But we couldn't find one. And we rowed across to a neighbor's cottage, a man I know well and respect, too: and we broke open his kitchen door and rummaged all through his cottage, in bins and boxes, under things and through things, but never a hammer could we find.

"Let's," said Jim, with a wild light in his eye, "let's go breaking into cottages all along the shore until we find a hammer."

"No, sir," I said. "No, sir. This man would let me break into his cottage the way I'd let him break into mine. But there isn't another cottager on this lake that I would let break into my cottage."

"O.K.," said Jim, grimly, and we rowed back home.

"We can use the back of the axe," said Jim, "for a hammer."

They're So Easily Lost

But the axe was out on the wood-pile, where it had lain all winter, under the snow; its handle was cracked and broke when Jim tested it, and its back, or hitting face, was bruised and battered from having been used for various purposes for 30 years.

"I can use a stone," I submitted, Jim grasping the axe possessively and not offering to lend it to me.

"Now," said Jim, "let's see the plan."

So on an old shingle I drew a rough outline of the lean-to annex I was planning to my cottage, a nice little kitchen that would allow another room to be used in the cottage proper. With the saw we cut scantlings for the frame, the floor, the walls and the roof. We sawed four scantlings and tied them up, by hand.

"Now," said Jim, "hand me a fistful of four-inch spikes."

And while Jim smoothly and steadily nailed the uprights and

laid the floor beams I went and got a nice round granite rock about the size of a spanish onion and proceeded to nail on the crosspieces, the stringers as Jim called them professionally.

About the ninth nail I was getting too expert and the rock I was using for a hammer slipped violently off a treacherous nailhead and jammed my finger dreadfully. It was a throbbing, aching, stabbing feeling that went right to my eardrums.

"Don't keep spinning round," yelled Jim, angrily. "Stand still and squeeze your wrist."

But it felt better if I kept spinning round.

"Awfff," said Jim, disgustedly, and smacked the spike he was driving with the axe-butt. And it slipped and caught him on the thumb something dreadful.

"Owwwww," moaned Jim softly, and he stepped slowly down off the scaffolding and started turning round and round with me, speaking low and dramatically all the while.

So we went out and sat on the veranda. It was a soft afternoon, the kind mosquitoes love, along with men. At first we nursed our fingers and then we waited and watched for some passing boat to come by so that we could send a message to the Landing for a couple of hammers to be sent up by motor boat.

But when no boat came by, we decided that if a boat came by, we wouldn't send any message: we would go ourselves, and get the hammers and come back.

But when no boat finally came at all we decided to heck with it, and we packed up our bags and stowed the nails and paint and stuff in the cottage, locked it up, piled our stuff into the rowboat and, favoring one hand each, took turns at rowing back down the lake to the Landing.

And there was Percy, as large as life and twice as merry, who gave us a royal welcome and helped us with our bags into the car and examined our injuries and put iodine on them, and vowed he would have the annex up by the next week-end, just to cheer us up.

"And," said Jim, "if you see that neighbor who lives in the cottage immediately to the east, just tip him off that there is no hammer in his cottage."

"Oh," said Percy. "I go around in the fall and pick up all the hammers lying around the cottages. They're so easy lost. So I store them, I'll be distributing them back around the proper cottages next week some time."

Some Other Time

"**O**ut in front of my place," announced Jimmie Frise, strolling in my back gate, "there is a great big pile of stone."

"So what?" I inquired

"Well," stated Jim, "it's there, and I didn't order any stone."

"Maybe it is some neighbour's," I offered.

"It's right on my lawn," announced Jim, with some astonishment. "Neatly stacked right on the lawn."

Jim hauled ahead and I wobbled and staggered along between the shafts of the barrow ... "We'll have to make it snappy," said Jim.

"What kind of stone?" I asked.

"Regular stone," described Jim. "Stone for building or for rock gardens or for the flagstone paths or anything."

"When was it delivered?" I asked.

"Nobody knows," said Jimmie. "I've asked all around the neighbourhood, and nobody knows anything about any stone. All I know is my family looked out the window and there was the pile of stone."

"Well, that's a funny one," I admitted. "Don't you remember telling anybody that you'd like some stone? Maybe you just happened to drop the remark some time lately and some friend of yours has sent you a present of stone."

"No, sir," stated Jim emphatically. "I certainly didn't. Because if there is anything in the world I don't want, it's a pile of stone. Here's my family already agitating for me to build a rock garden. And I have always said, if there is one thing I don't want it is a rock garden."

"You had better leave the pile," I decreed, "and whoever owns it will turn up and claim it. Probably it has been delivered to the wrong address."

"And meantime," cried Jim, indignantly, "my lawn is being ruined. I guess not."

"Well, what are you going to do about it?" I demanded.

"Well, it's got to get the heck off my lawn, that's all," declared Jim, hotly. "I called the police and they said they wouldn't know about a thing like that. If it was piled on the pavement, they could take action. But since it is on my lawn, that is my affair."

"Jimmie," I exclaimed, "there is a reasonable explanation for all things. Don't be hasty. Call up the various dealers in stone and sand and gravel and you'll find that somebody has either delivered it to the wrong address or else somebody has sent you a gift. Maybe there will be a letter in the mail to-morrow morning informing you that you have won a load of stone in a raffle. Did you buy any raffle tickets lately?"

"Oh, I'm always buying twenty-five-cent raffle tickets," admitted Jim, feeling in his pockets and bringing out little odds and ends of folded paper and looking at them one after another with surprise. "But I don't recall any raffle tickets about a load of stone. Unless . . ."

A Tough Problem

"Unless it was that church raffle," thought Jim, intently,

"where they had a ton of coal and a radio and a pair of hand-made patchwork quilts..."

"That would be it," I assured him. "That's what you've done. You've won a raffle."

"Well, what the dickens," protested Jim. "What do I want with a great pile of stone?"

"What do you buy raffle tickets for?" I countered.

"I buy them to get rid of the guy," admitted Jim, "the same as you or anybody else."

"My dear boy, a load of good stone costs money," I informed him. "You could sell that stone for maybe five or 10 bucks."

"That's an idea," said Jim brightly. "Who will buy it? Do you want any stone?"

"I could do with some stone," I admitted, looking around my garden. "I've sometimes thought of a rockery. Or maybe a flagstone path along here."

"O.K.," cried Jim, "it's a deal. How much will you give me for my stone?"

"Not so fast," I informed him. "I can get a ton of stone for four dollars, delivered right to my garden, down the side drive. Dropped on the spot, so to speak for four dollars."

"Hmmm," said Jim.

"In fact," I pointed out, "that stone you've got is, roughly 150 yards from here. It would have to be transported. Who would transport it?"

"Not me," agreed Jim. "For any four bucks."

"In fact," I mused, "supposing I did take your stone, as a favour, so as to relieve you of it and save your front lawn from damage, I wouldn't figure on paying for the stone; I'd figure on being paid for removing it."

"I'll pay nobody," stated Jim warmly. "They can't do this to me. They can't just come over and drop a load of stone all over my front lawn. No, sir. And put all kinds of notions in my family's head. Why, at this very minute I'll bet they are all out in the backyard planning where I'll build a rockery."

"You could collect damages," I supported. "You could collect damages for mental anguish and the estrangement of your family's affections and all kinds of things."

"Besides wrecking my lawn," agreed Jim.

"What you had better do," I suggested, "is go and telephone around the sand and gravel men and offer them the load for nothing if they will come and pick it up. If you leave it there, indefinitely, you will certainly have to do something about it. Either you will have to haul it into your yard and build a rockery or else take it and pile it on the pavement, so bringing the matter to the attention of the police. Then something will be done.''

"And meantime," Jim added, "my grass will be getting all yellow from the stone being piled on it.''

"Go ahead," I suggested, "go and call up some sand and gravel men and offer it to them for nothing. And then, after they have picked it up, I might make them an offer to drop it here in my side drive.''

"Ho," said Jim, eyeing me suspiciously.

"Sure," I admitted. "I'll be interested in that load of stone as soon as it is on board a truck. But not before.''

I'm on the Spot

So while Jim was gone back down to his house, I set briskly to work studying the garden to see just where a rockery would look best. I figured a small rockery in the southeast corner would look pretty smart, and if the stone were not too lumpy, I might run a sort of flagstone walk across the bottom end of the garden, a kind of courtyard or close of flag stones, like the pictures in the fashionable magazines of financial wizards' gardens. In fact, the longer I studied the proposition the more I wanted some stones. A garden is funny that way. Just let the seed of an idea drop into your mind when you think of gardens and, by George, that seed sprouts as if it were in a garden in reality. With a stick I traced in the sod the outline of a flagstone court at the foot of the yard; and in the corner where the rockery would be, I pulled out a few of the less valuable seedlings, in preparation for the clean-out that would be necessary to make way for the stone.

Jim was gone quite a long time. And when he came back, he came briskly.

"Look," he said, "I'll be frank with you. I called up six different dealers and none of them were open after supper. Then I got a seventh, who said it wouldn't pay him to pick up the load, as the big expense in stone is the handling. He's got lots of stone already loaded.''

"What would he charge to transport it 150 yards?" I asked.

"He said he was too busy to handle a small order," stated Jim. "In fact, I offered to pay him for transporting it for you.''

"My dear boy, that was very decent," I cried. "But I wouldn't think of letting you do that.''

"To be frank," said Jim, "I'm on the spot. My family have been out and figured the whole thing out. We're to have a rock garden."

"Aha," said I, disappointed.

"So I've got to act quick," said Jim excitedly. "What kept me was I drove them all down to the movie. Before they get home, that pile of rock has got to be out of there. Do you want it or don't you?"

"Sure I want it," I assured him. "But how can we . . ."

"We can do it," cried Jim. "There's a fellow down the street who has a wheelbarrow. With the two of us working, I figure we can shift the whole pile in two hours. In less than two hours. Come on."

"Wo-ho," I protested suspiciously. "It's a lot of work. Why don't you just wheel it into your own yard? I mean, of the two evils, building a rockery in your yard seems a lot less than wheeling all that stone up here."

"It's the principle of the thing," said Jim. "I don't want any rockery. And besides, you wouldn't help me. Whereas, if I gave you the stone, you'll be willing to help me get it out of the way."

"I don't like this haste," I informed him.

All Figured Out

"Look," cried Jim impatiently. "Once you give in, in this garden business, you're sunk. This rockery is the beginning. If I get a rockery, it means two rockeries, it means flagstone paths and everything. It means planting and buying special rockery plants. I know. I've watched my neighbours."

"Yet you expect me to build a rockery?" I argued.

"Ah, you're different," said Jim. "You've given in long ago to this garden stuff."

"Oh, have I?" I snorted.

"Listen," hissed Jim, "do you want the stone or don't you? In one hour and 50 minutes, I've got to pick them up at the movie. Between now and then, that stone is going to be gone from my lawn. Do you want it?"

"Yes," I admitted, high-pressured. "But where will you tell the family it went?"

"I'll say the truck driver left it by mistake and came and took it away," said Jim, desperately.

"O.K.," I muttered, being a family man myself.

"I'll just be five minutes, getting the wheelbarrow," shouted Jim, already sprinting down the drive. "Come on down and see the stuff."

So I slipped in and changed to my old shoes and then strolled down to Jim's. A pile of stone it was, indeed. Lovely limestone gray and coloured building stone of the best quality. No pick-up stuff out of a river bed, this. It was stone fit for a mansion or a public building. And there must have been two tons or more, a regular truck load of it.

While I was still estimating how many barrow loads of it there were, doubtfully, Jim came noisily up the street, on a fast walk shoving a big barrow.

"Jim," I protested, "we can never get all this off of here in two hours."

"Of course we can," cried Jimmie. "If we hop to it. Two of us on the barrow."

'Taking turns?" I asked. "And resting?"

"No, no, I've got it all figured out." exclaimed Jim, throwing off his coat. "You're the shortest. You hold the handles of the barrow and I'll walk ahead, hauling on it. My long legs would tilt the barrow too high for it to hold a good big load. Have you any gloves?"

"No," I muttered.

"Well," said Jim, "we haven't time to bother. Let's get at it."

Jim leaped with a will into the stone pile and laid in four chunks before I had shifted two and then I picked up the barrow handles.

"That's no load," protested Jim.

"It's load enough," I growled, starting to push.

Jim leaped ahead and caught hold of the front of the barrow and hauled. A wheelbarrow is not really one of the larger of human inventions. It may have served its purpose back in the dim and blundering past, before men did any real thinking. But it is pitiful to think of all the generations of mankind who have been warped and twisted out of shape by wheelbarrows, think of how tall and beautiful and straight the human race might have been by now? They might have been gods by now, but for the barrow. It drags at the shoulders, the arms, the back. It bends the legs and causes the feet to be flat and large and splayed. It bursts the muscles of the neck and causes the blood vessels of the head to bulge. It makes the eyes stick out and the ears to sing. It constricts the lungs and strains the viscera. It makes a man thick and squat, like a gorilla. Rather than believe that the human race is descended from monkeys, I am inclined to think that ages of pushing wheel-barrows has brought man down to the level of gorillas.

Too Late to Retreat

We made a fast trip, with the first load. There is a little terrace from Jim's lawn requiring that we push the barrow up to it, to avoid bumping heavily up or down three concrete steps. It was this terrace that was the hardest point in our short journey from Jim's lawn to my garden.

"My legs are too long," pleaded Jim. "A wheel-barrow really calls for a short man."

"We'll take turns," I informed him sternly.

Jim hauled ahead and I wobbled and staggered along between the shafts of the barrow. We took five loads, and the rock pile did not seem to be even nibbled. Only one edge of it appeared to be slightly reduced.

"Seventeen minutes," gasped Jim. "We'll have to make it snappy."

"My hands are blistered already," I informed him "

The sixth return trip, a large gray empty truck was just backing up to Jim's lawn.

"Oh, oh," muttered Jimmie.

It was too late to retreat, because a largish young man in overalls and a stoney face was already swinging down from the truck and saw uf.

"Hello," he called. "What's going on?"

"What's the idea," announced Jim loudly, "of dumping a lot of rock on my lawn?"

"My axle broke this afternoon," said the rough young man pleasantly. "I had to unload when the tow-truck called, I didn't think anybody would mind for a couple of hours."

"A couple of hours?" cried Jim. "Why, that stone has been there long enough to a whole lot of things to happen."

"You've taken some of it away," said the young chap, while an even larger and stonier man came down out of the truck cab, drawing on big gauntlets.

"We've moved five barrows of it," I said dryly, and a little gladly.

"You'll have to bring it back," said the young fellow, "this load is by weight "

"Bring it back, heck," said Jim. "You go and get it."

"Oh, is that so?" replied the youth. "How about me calling the cops and reporting a couple of old guys stealing my stone when my back was turned?"

"And I'll report that you dumped stone on my lawn, ruining it," shouted Jim.

"Excuse me," I said, "but if you'll drive around to my side drive, you can pick up the two or three measly barrow loads we've taken."

"O.K., sir," said the young fellow, recognizing a gentleman.

So Jim and I walked down the street to restore the barrow to its owner, while the two hearty lads thundered the big rocks back into the truck by hand.

"Well," sighed Jimmie, "men like us need a little unusual exercise now and then."

"We sure get it," I mumbled.

The following stories originally appeared in
the Star Weekly *on these dates:*

GANGWAY – October 15, 1938

ICED DUCK – November 5, 1938

SECOND BEST TURKEY – December 24, 1938

ONLY TWENTY DAYS – December 3, 1938

CIGARS ALL ROUND – January 14, 1939

MRS. I. WALTON – May 6, 1939

"Saved," I muttered and steered straight for the haystack ...

Gangway!

"**O**H," sighed Jimmie Frise, "to just keep right on driving and never come back to all the trouble and anxiety."

We were driving in the country looking for a certain extra large pumpkin we had read about in the papers.

"What do you mean, trouble and anxiety?" I demanded scornfully.

"The whole world," sighed Jim sadly. "The whole world."

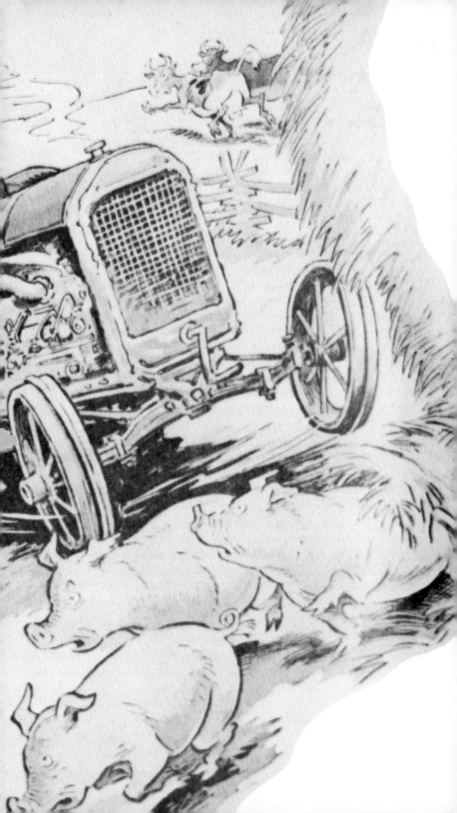

"The world," I informed him, "is in the condition that it deserves to be in. All the disturbances today are the result of counter-disturbances of yesterday. Push a man down and he jumps twice as high when he comes up. We have only ourselves to blame."

"A lot of people are talking like that these days," retorted Jim. "And just what do you mean by it? Do you mean that after the last war we should have gone into Germany and taken them by the hand and danced ring around a rosey?"

"Precisely," I stated.

"Puh," argued Jim.

"'Until we become as little children,'" I quoted, "'ye cannot enter the Kingdom of Heaven.' There are too many whiskers and moustaches of one kind and another in the politics of today for us to get anywhere. In a far distant day, when all the world is killed off and assassinated and dead of starvation and aerial bombs, the fifteen or twenty persons who remain had better take hands and dance ring around a rosey or else...! And if eventually, why not now?"

"It's all very well to talk," said Jim, "but there are practical considerations. If Germany keeps on rising in power and solidarity where do we get off, in about fifty years?"

"Where do we get off anyway?" I inquired. "There is certainly nothing in the history of the world to suggest that we British should sit on top of the world forever."

"Don't talk like that," cried Jimmie. "It's un-British."

"It sure is," I admitted, "and un-Babylonian and un-Greek and un-Roman and un-Charlemagne and un-Spanish and un-Louis the Fourteenth."

"Are you hinting," demanded Jim, "that we have come to the end of British domination of the world?"

"We've had a swell innings," I gloated "from Elizabeth down to now. Elizabeth and her captains — Drake, Frobisher, Raleigh, Hawkins — and their old barnacled ships coming low in the water with Spanish gold, into the Thames, from right around the wide earth."

"Those were the days," admitted Jim.

"Low in the water," I cried, "and paintless from three year's storms at sea. And out the Thames come scurrying little ships with friends, to tell Frank Drake 'go to sea, go to sea, his Holy Majesty, Philip of Spain, has asked for your head and Elizabeth has promised it.'"

"I remember," whispered Jimmie.

International Mulligan

"And Frank Drake laughs and all his ragamuffins in ragged clothes laugh down over the ship's rail, and he keeps right heading up the Thames until he comes to the London docks."

"And then?" cried Jim.

"Down river comes the royal barge, with thirty oars painted gold and red, and on the barge Elizabeth and her gentlemen, the Cecils and the Howards and the rest; and they pull in alongside the salt-caked ship, low in the water with all the Spanish gold. And Elizabeth walks up the greasy stone steps and across the gangplank and after into the cabin, where Frank Drake stands, bareheaded, with a grin."

"Didn't he bow?" asked Jim.

"Sure, he bowed, and then stood straight. So Elizabeth, in a frosty voice that Queens and Kings use when they are going to have a joke, says: 'Captain Drake, my cousin, his Holy Majesty, Philip of Spain, hath demanded of me your head.'

"Drake bows."

" 'Captain Drake,' she commands, high and haughty, 'kneel,' and Frank Drake kneels. 'Give me your sword,' she says to one of her Cecils. And a sword comes sweet and soft out of a velvet and leather scabbard. Elizabeth steps forward and strikes Frank Drake on the right shoulder.

" 'Rise,' cries Elizabeth, 'Sir Francis Drake!' "

"Oh golly," breathed Jim.

"And then they laugh and chatter and spend hours going over the ship and looking at the chests full of gold and strangeness, and hearing from Frank Drake and all his lads the story of the great voyage, around and under and up and back. And that was the beginning of the British story; that was the dawn of to-day; and all that went before were only the yesterdays that made us men."

"What do Germans or Frenchmen have of that sort of thing?" cried Jim. "They don't understand. We've got something. It can never be taken from us."

"But," I explained, "we can give it away."

"How give it away?" asked Jim.

"By throwing what we've got into the common pot and letting it all boil up into a sort of international mulligan, instead of hanging on to good old roast beef," I elucidated. "We're losing our taste for roast beef. Even our kids prefer hamburgers and weiners.''

"By jiminy, I see what you mean," said Jim. "I wish we had somebody we could cheer for on our side, somebody we would all run out of see passing in the street.''

"We're not much for cheering," I explained. "Frank Drake died on his ship at sea. Raleigh had his head cut off in the Tower. Roast beef doesn't generate cheers the way sauerkraut and spaghetti do. We cheer for ourselves all right. But not very heartily for individuals.''

"I wish the world would settle down," wished Jim.

"You might as well ask the ocean to settle down," I retorted. "It never will, so you might as well build a good big safe boat. Maybe it is a good idea to try and persuade all other boats to travel the same time and go the same way as ours. Maybe it would be a comfortable thing to get all the ships on the sea to tie themselves together into one big raft, against the anger of the ocean. But where would we get? No, sir. Get a good big ship and keep her in shape, that's the answer to the sea of human life.''

"And a good pilot," said Jim.

"And plenty of other good pilots, in the making," I pointed out.

Powers Not Understood

"You hate the idea of one man running the whole thing," protested Jim.

"I hate anybody being in control of powers," I stated, "which he may not wholly understand.''

At that moment a farmer, standing beside the snake fence, began waving at us eagerly.

"Hullo," said Jim, "a gentleman in distress.''

I slowed the car.

"Do you gentlemen happen," called the farmer, "to have a wrench handy? I've left mine up at the farm.''

"Sure," said Jim, who always is generous in my car.

I clicked off the engine and got out to loosen the front seat and dig under for the wrench. Jimmie had to get out, too.

"This tractor of mine," said the farmer, indicating a dilapidated engine with a gang of plows attached, "is acting up.''

I walked over and handed him the wrench. Suppose, I thought, we had been in a hurry? Or maybe the farmer could tell by the way we were driving that we were merely hunting up a certain extra large pumpkin.

"I'll just be a second," said the farmer, hurrying across the clods to the old tractor. It was a heck of an old tractor. About a model 1918, I should imagine. Not one of those little streamlined caterpillars of today, but a sort of steamroller of yesterday.

"Let's go and see," said Jim, legging over the snake fence. So there being no sense in standing aloof, I climbed over, too.

"I bought her," said the farmer, "from my neighbor. I've envied him this tractor for fifteen years."

"Does she work all right?" asked Jim.

"She works fine," said the farmer, "except you got to tinker with her now and then. She started missing, back there on the slope, and she quit here, just on the rise. I think she's got some dirt in the carburetor."

So we watched, with that absurd interest we assume in things of which we have no knowledge, while the farmer unscrewed a nut, loosened a copper tube, blew through it, stuck his finger in places and wiped around, examining the sludge with sharp attention.

"There," he said, "I think she'll go now."

He cranked the engine. The old tractor wheezed but did not fire.

"It takes a few minutes to get it through her head what you want out of her," explained the farmer, "but once she catched on, she fairly hums."

He cranked and cranked.

"Maybe," suggest Jim, "she's out of gas."

"I put three gallons in her last night," said the farmer, examining the gas tank. "She's got a good two inches in her yet."

"How did she die?" inquired Jim.

"We just started up this slope," described the farmer, "and she gave a couple of sudden coughs and stalled."

"It sounds like ignition," said Jim. "Take a look at the spark plugs. I'll glance over the wiring."

Jim went in close and pulled and shoved at wires while the farmer unscrewed the sparkplugs with my wrench, not making a very good job of it, because the plugs seemed to be corroded in.

But after a while, he got them all out and Jim and he studied them minutely, wiping them off and making a couple of slight alterations in the set of the points.

Then they put them back in and Jim said:

"Now give her a whirl."

174

Runaway Monster

The farmer, all rested and full of expectation, took hold and swung.

A slight cough.

"Here," said Jim, "hop in the seat and handle the spark lever. That thing on the wheel."

"I don't know anything about these things," I protested.

"You know a spark lever," commanded Jim, "keep it retarded until she coughs and then shoot her over to the other side. I'm going to take a whirl at the crank."

The farmer, having yanked four or five violent ones, cheerfully stood aside for Jim. I climbed up the wheel and sat in the seat, which had a decayed old blanket on it.

"O.K.," I called, "switch's on."

Jim gave one yank. It had a kind of fancy twist on it.

With a loud staccato bark, the engine leaped to life, I threw the spark lever over and to my amazement the tractor lurched into motion.

"The clutch, the clutch," shouted the farmer, running alongside, the wallowing monster, "I left her in gear."

I glanced frantically for the foot brake, the hand brake, the clutch pedal and the ignition switch. Nothing was in its place.

The foot pedal I shoved down on gave way loosely under my foot and nothing happened. I turned a small level on the dash and the tractor took a terrific lurch forward and doubled her speed.

Jim was on one side, trying to get a good spring aboard the cab and the farmer was on the other, shouting to me and pointing, saying "the handle, the lever, the thing."

But as I steered a curving course across the newly-turned furrows, which were clay, the two got big globs of clay on their feet and fell behind. I had no time to do anything but keep my eye on the path the tractor was taking and to hunt frantically for the handle, the lever, the thing.

I got hold of one handle that looked like a brake, but it had apparently nothing to do with the engine. I turned what I hoped was the ignition switch and all it did was shoot violent backfires out the little exhaust chimney beside me.

I could feel the gang plows dangling and jangling behind. Ahead, I saw a good stout tree. I decided, as what fisherman would not, to run a course close alongside the tree and entangle the plows in it.

Straight for the tree I steered, hearing above the din of the tractor faint shouts. I swerved to miss the tree narrowly and thus hook the plows around it. But though I felt the plows engage on the tree, the tractor did not stop, and when I turned to look back to see that the plows had broken loose from the tractor, I inadvertently ran over a snake fence and found myself with a whole new field to explore.

In the middle of this field was a haystack.

"Saved," I muttered.

And steering with resolution for the haystack, I scared several cows in all directions and from under the edge of the stack frightened a number of terrified pigs.

With a solid but wholly comfortable sort of a grunt from the tractor, the engine and me, we came to a stop against the haystack.

And from behind, panting, came Jimmie and the farmer, all clodded of foot and perspiring.

"Did you kill the engine?" shouted the farmer.

"It stalled," I said, as I leaped nimbly down.

"Gosh hang it," said the farmer, "she doesn't back up. That's the only thing wrong with her."

"H'm," said Jim. "That's embarrassing."

"I guess," said the farmer scratching, under his hat, "I'll have to shift the haystack."

So we all shook hands and I took my wrench and the farmer went over the hill towards his farmhouse and Jimmie and I went back out to the car.

"I only wish," said Jim, "that Hitler could have seen this."

We had to smash a channel from decoy to decoy ... Jim's teeth were chattering and I was cold beyond all shivering.

Iced Duck

"I'm open," said Jimmie Frise, "this week-end for a final go at the ducks."

"Take some of your thicker-skinned friends." I replied.

"I can't get over your indifference to duck shooting," said Jim. "It is, in the opinion of the greatest sportsmen in the world, the cream of all outdoor sports."

"Duck shooting," I informed him, "is sheer bravado. Only men who get a kick out of showing how tough they are go duck shooting."

"Isn't it funny," mused Jim, "how a man can outfit himself with opinions in defence of his own ignorance?"

"Duck shooting," I went on, "is the last survival of the hair shirt instinct in humanity. In past ages men wore hair shirts to show what they thought was their piety. It was only the desire to show how tough they were. Duck shooting is the same. You love to suffer, in order to demonstrate the vigor of your character."

"Can't you grasp," pleaded Jim, "the delight there is in doing something entirely different from your normal life? Can't you imagine any joy in entering a world as strange and different from the everyday world as it is possible to enter?"

"I don't like being cold," I stated. "I don't like being wet or sleety. I don't like to have to sit like a frozen dummy for hours on end in an icy bog, with a wind whistling amongst rushes."

"The first delight of duck shooting," interrupted Jimmie, "is the getting up at 4:30 a.m. You think of it with horror. As a matter of fact, it is the strangest and most delightful sensation imaginable. Your whole being is astonished. Your body, your mind, your secret spirit, tingles with a queer, a fascinating joy, just to be up in this mysterious and unearthly hour."

"Maybe my nervous system," I suggested, "is too close to the surface of me."

"Then," went on Jim, "the going out, after a good hot breakfast, into the stormy night, the chill, the stars, the wind. The walking and the rowing out to the duck blinds. The setting out of the decoys, in the darkness and the little waves, seems to wake up in your deep heart some age old cunning, and it gives you the same lovely tingle as hearing, softly, the tune your mother used to sing to you when you were in her arms, a child."

"What a queer comparison to make," I protested.

"It's true enough," declared Jim. "Most of the deepest feelings in us are queer. And rightly so, because all our deepest feelings are the ones that have survived from time immemorial in us, handed down to us from our fathers, generation after generation, across uncounted ages. Yet in the past few hundred years we have been trying to squelch these ancient things in us in order to be, as they say, civilized. So what we say and do and think, as civilized beings, seems plain and open. But whenever the deep, ancient things in us stir we find them strange."

"We'll be a better race," I stated, "when we have succeeded in squelching those ancient things entirely. The day will come when nobody will go duck shooting, partly because it is idle to kill wild ducks when it is so easy to kill tame ducks. And partly because it is silly to go out and expose yourself to cold and discomfort and possible danger of pneumonia."

Two Philosophies of Life

"I see," retorted Jim. "So you're one of the new pacifists. It is not because war is evil that you would put an end to war. But because it is silly and expensive and uncomfortable."

"Precisely," I cried.

"Then in time to come," suggested Jim, "there will be no more fishing, eh? Or golf or any amusements except the indoor amusements?"

"Even the indoor amusements," I informed him, "will have to be pretty intelligent to get by. Playing bridge will prove to be silly, sitting up stiff in an uncomfortable chair, having to keep your mind alert ... it won't go. Mankind is moving definitely towards the understanding of life that they arrived at centuries ago in India and China. And that is, that life, at its perfection, is simply sitting perfectly still, doing nothing, feeling nothing."

"How about the Germans?" demanded Jim. "They don't believe in any such perfection. All the trouble the Germans have been to the rest of the world, in the last 50 years is because they believe so utterly in action, in discipline, in suffering, in exposing themselves to hardship, in living and dying dangerously."

"Sparta," I replied, "believed that, too. But what is Sparta? Just a word. A printed word. Nothing else of it remains. No statuary or vases, no literature, no philosophy or laws. Sparta terrified the whole Greek world in its time. But it was the rest of Greece, the terrified part, that handed down to us anything that we value of Greek civilization."

"Puh," said Jim, " this is all recent stuff, this Greek and Roman business. Just the other day. What I am talking about is the stuff that is in human nature for the past fifty million years. Because the Greeks or the Romans had certain experiences, are we to be guided by them? Because they succeeded or failed, just within the past couple of thousand years, are we going to base our whole system of life on their experience?"

"What other experience is recorded?" I demanded indignantly.

"Recorded?" cried Jim. "You mean on paper? My dear boy, that counts out all the most valuable experience of all, because writing is only a recent invention. How about the records of every human experience written in our very souls? In our minds and hearts and instincts. That's where you want to look for records."

"You," I exclaimed, " are striking at the roots of civilization.

Our entire world depends upon the written experience of humanity."

"Therefore," triumphed Jim, "if, in the past couple of thousand years, everything mankind has done has been in error, your whole world is founded on error."

"But error couldn't survive for two thousand years," I protested.

"Oh, couldn't it?" inquired Jim, sweetly, "Then how long do you say error can survive? Take a look around you at the world, before you answer."

"Look," I said, irritated, "what has this got to do with duck shooting?"

"Everything," said Jim. "Because you can choose between two philosophies of life. You can either sit at home this weekend, doing nothing, feeling nothing, sagged in a chair like Buddha himself, believing in your numbed and all but lifeless mind that you are at the moment achieving the perfection of life. Or else you can come duck shooting with me and feel the cold and wind, and be aware of your skin and your eyes and your ears; filled with mystery of time and space, of stars and shadows and, as dawn begins to break, of swift flying little squads of wild ducks, swishing past, while you sit, controlling even your cold-shudders, motionless as a stump, and the squad of ducks, seeing your decoys dim in the reeds, bank and turn and wheel, and come wings set and rigid, coasting down into range of your gun."

Swell Day for Ducks

"You make a very unfair comparison," I declared. "If I stay home, there are a hundred little things I can do. I can paste all this summer's fishing snapshots in my album. I can rearrange my book shelves, and index the latest acquisitions to my collections of early Canadian and American angling literature."

"Very worthy, very worthy," agreed Jim. "Pottering about with a paste pot, sighing over yesterday, thumbing through old withered pages of books written by men who were men of action, who a hundred years ago, fished all our noblest waters when they were wild, and shot ducks and passenger pigeons and wild turkeys....You think you are civilized. You are only debilitated, like our lakes and woods."

"I like comfort," I stated. "And so did cave men. I'm the natural man, not you."

"You're just getting a little feeble," retorted Jim.

"Do you mean to insinuate," I demanded, "that I couldn't sit out in a bog as easy as you? Do you suggest that you are more fit to stand a little wind and weather..."

Well, you know how it goes? Somebody is always trapping us by the old personality method. At any rate, with a gun borrowed from my brother, and in hip rubber boots borrowed from the garage man, and in woollen shirts and leather vests and canvas hunting coats and great clumsy slicker borrowed from my son, I waited in the cold rain for Jim to back into my side drive to pick up my dunnage bags and valises full of spare woollens, and shell boxes and all the equipment a normal man can think of taking with him at this time of year on a most unnatural undertaking. Including a hot water bottle.

"A swell day for ducks," gloated Jim, shoving open the car door heartily.

"And for the flu," I agreed. "It smells as if it were going to snow."

Thus, for a period of three hours, along deserted highways amid a forsaken world, we drove, the rain flooding and volleying eternally, and the short afternoon waning to an unpleasant and mischievous darkness, out of which raced glaring lights of unhappy vehicles, and the dim, unfriendly lights of towns and villages wrapped in November gloom.

Jim professed to love it all, the feeling of strong and virile isolation from a timid and withdrawn world. He talked about the art of wing shooting, of leading a duck so many feet per yard of distance per angle of flight. He raved about the flavor of wild duck believing that a split teal, broiled in a wire broiler over charcoal, cooked merely to a perfection that still permitted the juices to run, and served with boiled wild rice, boiled celery served only with butter, and hot dry toast, to be the supremest wild falvor the human palate could appreciate.

We came at length, at what seemed midnight but was merely 8 p.m., to a village at which we turned east and took a rain-sodden country road. This we followed with caution for six miles to a farmhouse where everybody had gone to bed but a jovial elderly man, our host, who fed us rather sketchily on some overdone cold meat of some description, a lot of big loose bread, butter so salty it stung and hard stewed crab-apples in pink sweet water.

Jim and Jake talked loudly of the morrow, and the wind increased and the rain quit, and when we stepped out before going up to bed, the air had got so cold it pinched our cheeks.

"Will they ever be flying in the morning!" cried Jim mightily.

"Will they ever," agreed Jake, heartily.

And he led us up a creaky stairs to a gloomy slope-ceilinged room with two unmatched beds between barren walls. So damply, strangely, uneasily into bed and the lamp blown.

But almost immediately, the lamp was relit, and there, shadowed monstrously on the walls, was Jake, whispering us that he had the kettle on, and we dressed. In damp wool, in scrapy, frigid canvas, we dressed, and, rubber boots clumping and flapping, we went down to a breakfast of coffee-colored tea, thick, dry-fried bacon, two eggs fried stiff and turned over, thoroughly saturated with bacon grease. Then, wiping mouths hastily, off into the night, at 18 minutes to 5.

Jake showed us the boat and shoved us off from shore, with a husky but hearty good-by, good luck. We had to tramp away a thin shell of ice that held the boat to the frozen mud shore.

"She's freezing," I shivered.

"The wind will get up before daylight," shuddered Jim.

With frequent peerings and bendings low, Jim steered a zigzag course across the sullen water, and we came at last to a sort of promontory of swamp and bulrushes jutting out.

"Drop out the decoys," muttered Jim.

I fumbled amidst the potato sacks full of damp decoys, unwound the stiff cord, and dropped them overboard at Jim's direction. Twenty. "Bluebills, all," said Jim. "But whistlers will come into them."

Then with a powerful drive of oars, Jim thrust the punt into the point of bulrushes, ice crunching sharply and startlingly under the bow.

Waiting for the Sunrise

"Lovely," I murmured. "Do we sit on the ice?"

"We sit in the boat," said Jim, and with the oar, he cracked the thin ice ahead and hauled the punt inward with grips of the tall bulrushes. When we had battled our way six feet in, Jim began cutting bulrushes and sticking them upright along the gunwales of the punt.

"Now," said Jim, "for daylight. We're at exactly the right time."

Dawn is praised by poets. But poets are seldom out in November. Through the spaces in the rushes, we gazed out at blackness. The wind had fallen completely. But it was bitter cold.

"Don't stamp your feet,' hissed Jim. "Squeeze them with your hand."

And a little later:

"Don't cough."

And, just as a faint and sickly pallor became visible on the sky, he said: "Now you have to sit really still."

I could barely see the decoys, immobile in the glassy water, a few yards out from the rushes. Far off, a gun barked, again and again. Quite close, two guns banged the still and frigid air. We strained our eyes out into the sky above our decoys. But nothing passed.

It seemed hours for the dawn to break through. The sky was leaden. The air was icy. Not a breath moved the driest rush tip.

"She sure is cold," whispered Jim.

"Ssssshhh," I warned fiercely, massaging my feet through the rubber boots.

Seven o'clock came and went. Daylight, ghostly and wan, came. Our decoys lay inert and motionless on the queerly still water, but now we had to keep low, for fear of being seen.

"On a day like this," whispered Jim, "they may fly a little late...."

"Whisht," I warned, both hands inside my innermost garment.

Eight o'clock, like an invalid in a chair, rolled slowly in. Passed, and at 8:30, Jim stirred noisily.

"Well," he said in a profane voice amid the silence, "I guess there's no use sitting here any longer. We'll pray for wind tonight, for the evening shoot."

We stood up in the punt, and she did not wobble.

"Ho, ho," said Jim, rocking the boat. But she did not rock.

"Frozen in," I suggested.

So with the oars, we cracked the thin shell of ice around the punt, and, with Jim in the bow like George Washington, we broke a narrow passage out of the rushes. For 20 feet out, a lovely thin sheet of ice had frozen in the three hours of dawn.

Our decoys were fast in it. We had to smash a channel from decoy to decoy. Jim making the passage, I picking up the wooden beasts and winding the stiffening cord around them, after chipping off the fringe of ice.

Jim's teeth were chattering and I had reached the stage of cold that is beyond all shivering.

"I think," I said, carefully, "that my circulation has stopped."

"We'll be back in by the fire in 15 minutes," clicked Jimmie.

So like two Buddhas, we sat by the fire until 4 p.m., and then, no wind having risen and the sheet ice being 40 feet out from the muddy shore, we packed up roughly, and in the dark, drove home slowly, on a slippery pavement.

Second Turkey

"I 'M heading for the market,"
said Jimmie Frise. "Want to
come?"

"What's doing at the market?" I
inquired.

"I've got to buy a turkey," said Jim,
"the best turkey in the market."

"A turkey?" I exclaimed. "Then
what was that enormous nude figure I
saw hanging up in your back kitchen
this morning?"

"Ah, that's our turkey," explained
Jim. "But this one I've got to buy is
for an old friend of the family, an old
lady I've been giving a Christmas
turkey to now for nearly 20 years."

"That's kind," I submitted. "The
true Christmas spirit. We should
always remember the poor old ladies."

Best

Finally we came back to the good one Jim had spotted in the first place; and bought it.

"Poor old lady my foot," laughed Jim. "This one is no poor old lady. She's got a lot more dough than you and me together She's a very comfortable old party, very comfortable indeed."

"Aha," I laughed back, "Rich old lady gets Christmas turkey, Jimmie Frise gets ten thousand dollars."

"No chance," said Jim. "She gets the income from an estate and every cent of it goes to her children when she dies. But she's such a lonely old soul, we just started this turkey business after the war and now she expects it, as regular as her cheque from the trust company. She wouldn't buy a turkey if we didn't send her one."

"What kind of a person is she?" I protested. "Some kind of old crank?"

"Oh, no she's all right," explained Jim, "but she just doesn't get on with people. Her children and so forth. But it doesn't hurt us to send her a turkey and she gets a tremendous kick out of it. It gives her the Christmas feeling, I guess."

"It's funny," I said, "the people who think they are entitled to feel the Christmas spirit."

"I always get her," said Jim, "the finest and biggest turkey I can find. It gives me a queer feeling to send her such a turkey. She can't ever use it. A little turkey, even a little chicken, would be enough for her. But being reasonable at Christmas seems sort of blasphemous to me. To really feel Christian, you ought to overdo things. You ought to carry things to excess. It's a form of humor. The divine humor that sent hosts of angels to sing and shout the good tidings of great joy, not up the main streets and into the better-class residential districts, but to shepherds minding their flocks by night, out on the cold and lonely hills. How about it? Would you like to come?"

So we went to the market, and a great place it is, Christmas week. So crowded with provender, there is hardly any room for the buyers. And it has a great country smell to it, and the cold is so sharp and the sense of bounty so lavish. It is not like going into a store, where the turkeys are in one section and the cabbages in another. You can see all kinds of separate and distinct exhibitions of turkeys, as though it were an art show, and each man had his own chef d'oeuvres by themselves. You struggle slowly through the narrow crowded aisles, gazing upon great displays of hung turkeys, some pallid, some rosy, some bloated, some lean, some neatly killed and some killed as though by a sledge hammer on the head. And all of them aloft above an earthly array of every conceivable vegetable and fruit, offered in country simplicity without guile or art.

Red Ribbon and Gold String

"Don't let's be in a hurry," said Jim. "I want to buy my turkey, knowing it is the biggest and best in the market. That is a most important part of this gift."

"I can't understand you going to such bother over a cranky old lady," I submitted. "It is cold and it's damp in here. Let's get going. There's a dandy big bird, right there."

"Too old," said Jim. "Tough as shoe leather. Dry as punk."

He thrust his way down the aisle and I followed in the wake he made amidst the crowd. He stopped and studied every turkey display, large and small. He leaned out and felt the bulging breastbones. He squeeze their meat, pinched the skin.

"There's a beauty," he admitted at last. "There's a real Christmas turkey. Look at it. Look at the shape. The color. Feel the skin."

"O-kay, take it." I said, adjusting my muffler better, because the market chill was penetrating me.

"Not until I've been around and made sure," said Jim.

"Aw, what the heck is this?" I called sharply.

"It's a ceremony," said Jim. "An old lady who doesn't deserve it, is getting a lot of attention. And the best of it is, she will never know about it. All she gets is a turkey. But look what I get out of it."

"I don't see it," I declared, following him again.

"Plenty wouldn't," agreed Jim.

So round and round the market we struggled, in the far corners, down the main aisle, and finally, after most thoroughly scrutinizing every turkey on display, we came back to the good one Jim had spotted in the first place; and bought it. At a price that was considerable. The farmer wrapped it with the special care farmers take in wrapping things up, and always vainly. For when he handed the monstrous package over the rough counter, turkey was protruding out of it in sundry places. But that's the best part of parcels from the market.

Out to King St. we labored our way and into the car and back to the parking lot near the office. Jim locked the car doors carefully and we went back to the office for such work as a man can do Christmas week, with everybody coming in to see us and everybody telephoning from home to remind us what we have to bring home, and nobody's mind on work anyway.

And at 5 p.m., we proceeded out into the night to go home in

Jim's car. There was the mighty turkey, safely at rest upon the back seat.

"Let's see," said Jim, "did we have anything else to get before we go home?"

"Not me," I stated.

And Jim, as though there was something on his mind, slowly got in behind the steering wheel and we drove down to the Lake Shore.

Half way home along that crowded and wintry highway, Jim suddenly cried:

"Ribbon."

"Stickers," I retorted.

"Hang it, I was told to bring home ten yards of red ribbon," said Jim, as we bowled along in the traffic.

"And I was told to bring home a packet of Christmas stickers," I confessed.

"We'll turn up to Queen St.," said Jim. "There are lots of little stores along there."

So we edged out way out of the homing traffic and turned up one of the northerly exits from the Lake Shore and made our way to Queen St., at one of the sections of it filled with little stores, no less bright and ay than downtown.

"Get me ten yards of narrow red ribbon," said Jim, as I got out at the first space we came to.

I entered a little shop and got the ribbon and two packets of assorted stickers, when the door opened with a jangle of bells and Jim came in.

"Gold string, too," he said. "I forgot. A ball of gold string."

So we got that and crossed the jamming traffic to our car and got back in.

"The turkey!" shouted Jim.

The turkey was gone.

Yes, sir, in less than three minutes, that turkey had been snaffled right off the back seat of the car. With the streets jammed and bright and roaring.

We leaped out and looked furiously in all directions. In a doorway, an elderly lady, who was sweeping slush off the step, signalled us:

"A young boy took a package out of that car," she called. "I spoke to him, but he said he was to deliver it across the street."

"What did he look like?" Jim demanded.

"A nice young chap," said the woman. "About 18 or so. A very nice-mannered boy."

"Which way did he go?" I cried.

"Why, he walked right across the street, heading a little off that way," said the lady, indicating east with her broom.

"Come on," commanded Jim.

"He can't be far ahead," I submitted, as we dodged across the street.

"He can't run with that parcel," gasped Jim, running, "but we can."

So we ran, ducking and nipping in and out of the street crowds, and keeping a sharp eye in all directions and in the store windows.

At the first corner, we asked a newsboy if he had seen a young fellow going by with a big parcel.

"Sure," he said, "a guy just went up there in a hurry. With a turkey, I think."

"That's him," shouted Jim, and up the dark little old street we galloped. Ahead, we made out a few pedestrians going and coming and a long way up, one figure in particular, a half-running figure and in his arms some kind of a load.

We ran. As we gained on him, he turned sharply into a sidewalk, and as he did so, we stopped running instantly, and made note of which house he was entering. When he disappeared, we began to run again until we came abreast, approximately, of the place he had turned. It was a shabby little narrow house, one of a dozen alike.

"I think it's this one," panted Jim.

"Take it easy, get our wind," I gasped. So we walked up the pavement and stood in the shadow of the front door, and shadowy it was.

"The thief," I muttered. "The dirty snatcher."

"Young toughs," panted Jim. "pinching Christmas turkeys right out of cars...."

"Will we turn him in? Should we get a cop first?" I asked.

"Get the turkey, before he hides it," corrected Jim in a low voice. "Then we can report it. Probably some young gangster. Our word will be enough."

Jim, peering and finding no bell, rapped loudly on the old blistered door.

No answer. He rapped loudly again.

"Footsteps," whispered Jim.

A light came on in the vestibule, there was a fumbling at the lock; and the door opened. There before us, silhouetted against the light, was a young fellow of about 17, still in his overcoat.

"We'd like to speak to you, me lad," said Jim, sternly, pushing in. The young fellow backed ahead of him and I followed.

"Where's the parcel?" demanded Jim, quietly, for fear of bringing tough reinforcements from the back of the house, where, from behind closed doors, sounds of excitement came. "Where's the parcel you carried in here a minute ago?"

"What," said the young scoundrel, in a thick, husky voice, "what kind of a parcel, mister?"

"A turkey," said Jim, "wrapped in newspapers."

The young fellow stood motionless in the pallid light and his head was hung so we could not see his face. It was a thin face. A thin, rather fine looking face on a young man so shabbily dressed, in coarse work clothes.

"Come on," I said sharply.

"I'll," he said, barely audible. "I'll go get it."

"Make it snappy," I repeated.

But still he stood, motionless, as if his legs were turned to lead. Still his hand was on the doorknob, clenched and white. And slowly he lifted his face. I do not suppose I should say it was a beautiful faces. It is not right to say thieves have beautiful faces. But slowly he lifted it, not to us, but as if to God, maybe, and on it was a strange, white, thin, terrible expression of agony that I seemed to have seen before, somewhere, perhaps in old paintings was it, or maybe on little wooden carvings...

"Here," said Jim, "what's the matter?"

"Nothing," gasped the boy. But tears were soaking down over his thin cheeks. "Nothing."

He let go the door knob and tried to turn walk down the shadowy and narrow hall.

"Look here, a minute," said Jim, grasping the boy's sleeve. "Just a minute, kid. What's all this? What did you pinch our turkey for ?"

As if he hated to go down that hall, as if to open that distant door was to enter the presence of death itself, though sounds of life and joy came from behind it, he paused and turned, wearily, weakly.

"I don't know," he whispered. "I guess I went crazy."

"What do you mean?" I demanded, to see if my voice would still work in the presence of that thin and beautiful young face.

"We had a raffle, at the plant," whispered the boy.

"Oh, you've got a job?" Jim asked.

He nodded.

"What wages?" I inquired, for a stall.

"Six," said the boy, "six dollars a week, in the shipping."

"Go on," I said, making it stern, but it came out cracked a little around the edge.

"We had a raffle at the plant. It was for a turkey, and I told them I was going to win it for sure," said the boy, wearily. "We had the draw today, and I didn't win."

"Who's they?" asked Jim.

"My mother," whispered the boy. "My mother and kid sister, in there."

He nodded heavily back down that dim and terrible hall.

"So...' he leaned against the wall. "So, on the way home tonight, I happened to look in that car...I don't know what happened to me. I just don't know, I guess. I don't remember. I looked in...it seemed to be a turkey, a great big turkey...I opened the door, I grabbed it...."

And suddenly his head fell down on his chest, his hands went to his face and Jim's arm was around the boy's shoulders and I had hold of his arm, tugging at it to get his hands down from his face; and in a little while, for fear of disturbing anybody down that long, long hallway to death and disaster, we went out in the cool and reviving night, and stood on the dark steps and waited, not with many words, but with a lot of pats and slaps on the back and little swear words men use to show that they have hearts like steel; and when he was all straightened up and tidied, we shook hands with him as man to man, since all God's children have wings, and only by the grace of God are we not all thieves nailed to little crosses. And much slower than we came up, we went down that street and got into the car and drove to Sunnyside before either of us spoke.

Then Jimmie spoke first.

"The old lady," he said, "gets the second-best turkey."

Only Twenty Days

"**W**hat the dickens," inquired Jimmie Frise, looking up from a list he was writing, "can a father give a daughter of 20?"

"Why ask me?" I retorted. "What can a father give a daughter of seven?"

"For you it's easy," said Jim. "Wait until your kids grow up."

"The older they are, the more sensible they are", I pointed out. "You can give a young man of 20 something not very spectacular but full of value. But with young children, you have to make a splash."

*"Boy, what a bed," said Jim.
"We had one in the attic of the
farm and it was my favourite.
How much is it?"*

"You have to make a splash with a daughter of 20" assured Jim.

"Give her a wrist watch," I submitted.

"She's got a wrist watch," countered Jim.

"Give her a diamond - studded wrist watch," I offered.

"Oh, yeah?" retorted Jim. "Listen, I've got a family."

"Isn't it the dickens," I sympathized. "Jim, there ought to be a sort of upper-class social service bureau for Christmas advice. You ought to be able to send for a woman to come into your home, a trained Christmas expert, the same as a trained social service worker. She'd come and live right in your house for a day, studying the children, examining everything they possess and figuring out what they don't possess and what they need or what they want. And then she'd draw up your Christmas list for each member of the family."

"Both what they give," said Jim, "and what they get."

"That's it," I enthused. "It's a real idea. Maybe we could sell the idea to the big stores. A Christmas advice bureau, with a staff of young women to come and sit in with the family for a day, and then give expert advice."

"Most Christmas gifts," said Jim, " are so silly. We think only in terms of Christmas. Of winter. Of December. Now, I've wanted a new shooting coat for the past five years. I never can afford one in October, because I've spent all my money during the summer. Yet my family usually spends $12 on me, and you can get a swell shooting coat for $12."

"I'll bet the total of a man's Christmas presents," I declared, "comes to far more than that. I've wanted a new canoe for the cottage for years. But who would give me a canoe for Christmas? There's the fact that it couldn't be used for six months. There's the problem of storing it somewhere. There's the fact that they couldn't hang it on the Christmas tree. So they don't get me a canoe. They get me ties and socks and a new pipe and books, and tins of hundreds of cigarettes, and a whole raft of stuff, all of which would equal the cost of a new canoe."

"For instance," interrupted Jim, "my wife has been pining for a Persian rug for years. Every time we pass a store with rugs in the window, she just stops and stands paralyzed. She only wants one around $67.50 or something like that. Yet would I consider giving her a Persian rug for Christmas?"

"Why not?" I demanded.

"Because it's for the house," mocked Jim. "It's something

for the house, therefore it's barred from being a Christmas present. Christmas presents have got to be personal."

To Recognize Christmas

"Oh, no, they don't," I countered. "That's just a habit of mind a lot of us have got into. I know plenty of people who give new radios for Christmas."

"Yes," said Jim. "Childless couples. They can give each other things of mutual interest and value. But the mother of a family deserves something personal. Years ago, she gave up all thought of herself. In fact, the day her first baby was born, she thought her last personal thought. From then on, she has worked and schemed and planned and thought her whole life for others. Christmas is about the only time of year you can sort of square accounts with a mother."

"You're right, Jim," I agreed. "In fact, there's a thought there. Why not have a Christmas day for giving gifts only to mothers? Nobody but mothers get any gifts. The pleasure everybody else gets is in giving to mothers."

"That would be a good idea," said Jim, "only it forgets mothers. Because one of the greatest thrills in a mother's whole year is the giving at Christmas. Giving for the children, giving the children a whale of a day, giving them a feast...Why, when you come to think of it, Christmas is really mother's day, because it is the mother's most giving day in her whole year of giving." "Well," I submitted, "Christmas ought to be different, somehow. It is too seasonable. Too Christmassy. If it is going to be commercialized, and it sure is, then it ought to be reorganized on a better commercial basis. If a woman wants a Persian rug, Christmas ought to give it to her. You can give her something that will make her happy on Christmas or you can give her something that will make her happy in June and September and all the rest of the year as well."

"What have you in mind, besides canoes?" asked Jim.

"Well, my wife," I said, "is always going into trances in front of antique shops. She just loves old wood. Old walnut most of all. She loves chests and highboys and even whatnots. She loves old chairs and petit point and tables, all darkly gleaming."

"Don't you buy her any?" asked Jim.

"No, she's of Scottish descent," I explained, "and she always remembers the children. Children mar and smash and batter furniture. So we are saving antiques for when our children are all grown up."

"I love that antique stuff, too," confessed Jim. "When I think of the kind of furniture we have to live with, all because our kids are noisy and rambunctious."

"It's the radio," I explained. "You can't imagine a radio playing swing or giving us a new chapter in the daily career of Tough Burke, the boy detective, in a living room furnished in old walnut and lady chairs, such as our grandparents lived in."

"The dignity of life," sighed Jimmie, "is vanishing. Our lives have now to be furnished and equipped for sudden wild leaps of boys and sudden outbursts of dancing, and tommy guns firing from behind a barricade of chesterfield cushions piled on the floor, and parties springing up from nowhere, on account of the rapid transit of motor cars, with stains on the table and sandwiches crumbling and cigarette burns on the edges of the mantle."

"It's a heck of an age," I admitted, thoughtfully. "But do you know, I have a hunch that what I'll give my wife this Christmas will be her first nice little piece of antique walnut? A gateleg table or a chest of drawers."

"Start in a small way," agreed Jim. "And the older your children get, the more lovely old stuff you can acquire, so that by the time the kids are grown up you will be furnished throughout with stuff that is dignified and old and graceful and lovely."

"Yes, sir," I mused, "and I think that instead of a canoe, I'll start dropping hints around about that pair of early American squirrel guns that I showed you. Remember?"

"They're probably gone by now," said Jim.

"No, sir," I said. "I was in looking at them only the other day. Two genuine Kentucky squirrel rifles. Can you imagine how swell they would look, suspended over the fireplace in my den?"

"Fifty dollars, weren't they?" asked Jim, doubtfully.

"Only forty-five," I corrected. "And anyway, if I give my wife a walnut colonial table worth $50, shouldn't she go out of her way a little in regard to my present? Anyway, I've worked pretty hard this year, and I've given a lot of thought to my children, even if I haven't been with them much."

"I saw some rugs in that shop, didn't I?" asked Jim.

"Yes, you did," I recollected. "I noticed a big pile of them the last time I was in looking at those Kentucky rifles."

"Let's drop over there at lunch," suggested Jim.

Which we did. And I am unhappy to inform you that the Kentucky squirrel rifles, once in the collection of the famous Charles Noe Daly, were gone. The dealer had disposed of them to a man in exchange for a genuine Sheffield tray and $10.

"Why," I told him, "I was prepared to go as high as $50 for them."

"It's too bad," said the dealer. "But he took them and sold them to a collector in Chicago. I hear he got $150 for them."

"Mm, m'm," I retired.

As I started for the door, Jim hailed me.

"Here's rugs," he said. And I wandered back and watched him haul and lay rugs, many of them pretty seedy looking, the good ones being all around $675.

"Come along," I muttered.

"You go and look at colonial walnut tables and things," urged Jim, "while I go through these."

"I think I'll give my wife something more personal," I replied. "Lingerie or a house coat or something."

But Jim went on exploring in the pile of rugs and I wandered amidst the scattered treasures, looking at them without interest. They were the usual old, plain chests, wardrobes, tables, of all sizes; antique chairs, very uncomfortable looking.

Jim joined me.

"I didn't see anything I liked there," he said, "at any price I could afford. Do you see anything you like?"

"Those guns," I muttered. "Did you ever hear of such rotten luck? Imagine the guy selling them for a sheffield tray and $10."

"Look here," said Jim, suddenly excited. "Look at that bed!"

It was a battered, dull, knobbly little old bed.

"Isn't that a trundle bed?" cried Jim, excitedly. "Excuse me, mister."

The dealer came lazily down the room, the way antique dealers do. Some of the timeliness of their wares seems to enter into the bones of antique dealers.

"Isn't that a trundle bed?" cried Jimmie, pointing.

"That's what we call a string bed," said the dealer. "It is laced across with heavy cord for springs."

"That's it," cried Jim. "At home, we called it a trundle bed. See, there are little holes for threading the rope through."

And holding up the pieces of the old walnut bed, Jimmie and the dealer explained the primitive method by which our great-grandfathers achieved a little comfort. The sturdy four posts of the bed were mortised for the inset of the four boards that comprised the sides and ends. Then a powerful cord or leather thong was laced through the holes in all four boards, back and forth, a few inches apart, making a sort of mesh of cord. Springs, in fact.

"On top of these cords," explained Jim, enthusiastic and delighted, "you laid a thick feather tick. Boy, what a bed!"

"Did you ever sleep on one of them?" asked the dealer, very polite.

"We had one in the attic of the farm," cried Jim, "and it was my favourite bed. I slept my boyhood away on a bed like this. My, what memories it brings back. Isn't it a tragedy that we have disposed of all this lovely old walnut stuff, for a lot of brass and cheap plyboard furniture . . . How much is this?"

"That one," said the dealer, "not being in very good shape, I can let it go, just as it is, for $18."

"Eighty?" said Jim.

"Eight--TEEN," said the dealer, very honest.

The Trundle Bed

"I'll take it," said Jim, instantly. "I'll take it . Of all the dear old things. Just look at it. Look at this old walnut . . ."

And I had to help him turn the various pieces this way and that and examine them up near the window, to see the lovely grain of the wood.

"Our great-grandfathers," said Jim, "had no other furniture but this simple, stately, unpretentious colonial, perfect in its design, without ornamentation. Then came the late Victorian era, with everything stuffed and scrolly. They traded their old furniture for bird's-eye maple and light oak. Then came fumed oak. And all this glorious old stuff was sent to the attic or the cellar or given away to our poor relations, while we went garish and light and ornamented and scrolly, and twisty and altogether ridiculous."

"In other words, our great-grandfathers were right," I submitted.

"Now we are paying fat prices to try and get back," said Jim, "some of the stuff we threw away . . ."

So Jim paid his $18 for the trundle bed and arranged for it to be sent home. And we walked back to work, me thinking about old Kentucky squirrel rifles and peach-coloured lingerie and new ski boots for growing boys, and other seasonable thoughts.

After supper, Jimmie telephoned me. In a very low voice.

"Listen," he muttered, "have you mentioned that bed I bought to anybody at your place? Anything about the price?"

"No," I said, truly, for I hadn't thought of it since.

"Well, I'm in a bit of a jam," said Jim. "That bed I bought IS my bed. It's been in our attic for about 20 years. My wife gave it away to some social service workers only a week ago."

"Jim," I said.

"She got tired of it being in the attic, so she gave it away with a lot of old baby carriages and stuff," mumbled Jim. "So I told them I ran across it in an antique store and bought it for a dollar."

"Jim," I repeated.

"So you see, you've got to be pretty quiet about it," he continued.

"But Jim," I said, "it can't be your very own bed."

"It is," said Jim. "These social service workers probably sold it to the antique dealer because no poor family would have a feather tick."

"But it is probably just a coincidence," I submitted. "There are likely dozens of them around."

"No," said Jim. "It has got my initials carved in it with another pair of initials set in a heart."

"Oh!" I cried.

"Shhhh," warned Jim, low. "Some boyhood love affair that I tried to carve into eternity. I don't even remember who B.J. was."

"What are you going to do with the bed?" I inquired.

"I was wondering," asked Jim, "if you are still interested in giving your wife something antique for Christmas?"

"I was thinking of giving her a Persian rug," I replied.

"Okay," whispered Jimmie, and hung up the receiver.

...But then, quite suddenly, the storekeeper made a four-jump and got three kings out of nowhere.

Cigars All Round

"It will be a good three hours," said Jimmie Frise, "before he can get the clutch relined."

"Do you mean to say," I demanded, "that the whole clutch is gone?"

"It just went all of a sudden," explained Jim.

"Nothing in a motor car goes all of a sudden," I stated hotly. "If we'd been in my car this wouldn't have happened. Here we are stuck for three hours in a peewee village, on a nasty stormy night..."

"Curl up in the back seat of the car," suggested Jim, "and have a nap."

"I don't feel like a nap," I informed him "I feel like getting home to Toronto."

"Okay," proposed Jim, "you walk on and I'll overtake you presently and pick you up."

This absurd suggestion required no answer, because it was one of those nights of howling Arctic wind and snow drifting cold and wraithlike off the fields and across the bitter pavement of the highway.

"Maybe," said Jim, "we could get a cup of coffee and a sandwich. Wait until I inquire."

He went back into the gloomy garage where the garage owner was already disembowelling Jim's car. In a village the size of this one, it takes five minutes even to ask a man if there is any place to get a cup of coffee and a sandwich.

"No restaurant in this village," said Jim, finally coming out. "But there is a lady down the street a little way who runs a hot dog stand in the summer. He says maybe she would oblige us, unless she's gone to bed."

"It's only 8 p.m.," I protested, looking at my watch.

"Okay," said Jim, "let's go."

"I don't want a cup of coffee," I declared.

"Well, for Pete's sake," cried Jim, "what do you want? Here we are stuck, through a little misfortune that might happen any time..."

"Jim," I demanded, "why don't you have us towed to Toronto? These village blacksmiths don't know anything about clutches and things like that."

"It would cost $6 to have us towed," said Jim. "And this man can fix our clutch as good, maybe better than any city garage. In the city, my clutch would be only one of 17 clutches to be fixed at the same time. But here, it is the first clutch he has looked at since last September. I will get special attention."

"Maybe he has never seen a clutch before," I suggested.

"He says he has," said Jim, "and if I had to choose between this fellow, and a lot of apprentices and high pressure workers in a city repair shop, with a dozen clutch jobs to do before closing time, why I'd prefer this village mechanic. Think of all the old cars around here that he has to keep in operation."

"Then you brought that crate of yours to the right place," I agreed bitterly.

"Sometimes," sighed Jim, "I think you and I ought to always travel in separate cars."

"From now on," I retorted, "believe me, we will."

Craving Company
Jim stepped out the door of the garage office into the bitter

night and stood breathing deep of the air and gazing up and down the village street. I followed him.

It was a typical highway village. A church, a garage, a general store and about 10 houses, most of them one-storey frame cottages. Seven naked electric street lights served to illuminate the place. Through the branches of barren maples that in summer bower this little hamlet and make it a landmark for a million merry travellers, the winter wind moaned and blasted. Not a living soul was in sight. The only sign of habitation was a dim light glowing in the steamy windows of the general store.

"Let's go for a little walk," said Jim, very friendly.

So we turned up collars and stuck fists deep in pockets and bowed our heads and walked up past the store. We halted and looked in the windows, but nothing of merchandise was visible through the steam on the glass. There seemed to be the usual array of pails, axes, harness and some boxes of groceries.

Inside, we could see a couple of figures that moved and the sounds of human voices came distantly to our ears.

"Let's go in," said Jim. "I crave human company."

"Later," I said. "Wait until we get cold. Preserve this as our sole entertainment."

So we hunched up and walked briskly past three or four little dark houses and came to the end of the village. And we turned and walked back more slowly, past the store, the garage and so out to the farther end of the village.

"Isn't it ghastly to think," I said, "of these people living in self-imposed solitude? Look at it. Probably 50 people in this village. And it is as if they were dead and in their graves. Not a sound not a sign. Only three, four, five lights burning. What on earth are they doing?"

"Oh, they're happy," said Jim. "They're probably all busy in a quiet way. I bet there is a radio in every one of these homes. In what way does this village differ from Toronto?"

"Puh", I scoffed.

"In Toronto," said Jim, "they live in the front of their houses, that's all. There is a little more light."

"Oh, nonsense, Jim," I cried, "Think of the streets, at this hour, the shopping streets, full of people; the movie crowds; even the residential streets full of cars and everything."

"Nonsense to you," retorted Jim. "In Toronto, everybody is a slave. Rich and poor, all are slaves. They get up in the morning and rush to their labor. They labor in fear and trembling all day, the rich, trying to safeguard and increase their riches, the poor in fear for their daily bread. But, for a little hour or two each evening, they are free, or imagine they are. So they walk about, in the streets, pitifully, in the bright shopping streets, and go to the movies to lose themselves in dreams of love and freedom; and drive gaily about in their cars, from house to house, visiting and pretending to one another about the wide and varied interests of their lives. But all of them, the rich, the poor, remembering tomorrow, and the fatal grind, and the long, anxious day."

"It's chilly out here, Jim," I suggested.

A Social Centre

"But in this little village," continued Jim, "and in a thousand thousand little villages like this all over the world, there is peace and quiet and security. Not in the front, but in the homely back of these houses, men and women and children are engrossed in happy things, in reading, knitting, talking gently. There is no fuss and no pretence, for they need not pretend. Each home has its job for tomorrow, a simple and honest job. And it waits for them. And they for it. And because everything is quiet, including their consciences and their hearts, they can go to bed any time. They can go to bed now, at 8.15 p.m., because they do not have to stay up late, trying to extract some desperate interest from their lives."

"Huh, huh," I argued, halting and turning to walk back into the village to which we were condemned for nearly three hours more.

"You've got to look at something else than the front of houses," said Jim, getting in step. "In ninety-nine out of a hundred houses in cities, my friend, people are doing no more than these village people. But doing it hopelessly."

"Ho, hum," I concluded.

And we passed all the silent, dark little houses and came again past the garage, where we looked in and saw the mechanic darkly bent over the organs and entrails of Jim's car, laid out on a bench; and once more to the general store.

"Let's go in," said Jim.

"What for?" I inquired.

"Just to look around," said Jim. "You won't find these village stores like city stores, with a clerk dashing at you full belt. This is a sort of gathering place. City stores are purely mercantile. Village stores are social centres."

"Haw, ho," I subsided.

So we knocked our boots against the step and pushed open the door with its jangling bell.

It was warm and foggy. Down at the back end of the store was a stove and around it sat six men, all but one of them in their heavy winter coats and caps and mufflers. Temperature means nothing to the country, apparently. When you put on your winter clothes, you put them on, that's all. This store, dim and crowded with merchandise, with its hot stove humming, was stifling. But everybody had his heavy coat on and his hands in his pockets.

The one man without a coat was sitting at a little table around which everybody was grouped, and he rose, after Jim and I had stood for quite a moment in the gloom of the forward part of the store, and came towards us.

"Yes, gentlemen," he said, absently. "What can I do for you?"

"Do you keep cigarettes?" asked Jim.

"A few brands," said the storekeeper, still absently. "What kind do you fancy?"

Jim names his brand.

The storekeeper opened a showcase and hunted thoughtfully amongst the four or five kinds he had, all clearly visible. He named them over. He drew our a couple of different packets and studied them intently.

"No, I don't seem to have your kind," he said.

You would think a storekeeper would know what kind of goods he had.

"I smoke a pipe myself," he said, as if explaining.

"Well," said Jim, looking about.

Cordial Welcome

"Sorry," said the storekeeper. "Is there anything else?"

"No, I guess not," said Jim. "We were just stuck for time, having our engine fixed next door ..."

"Oh, come right in," said the storekeeper, with kindly understanding. "Make yourself at home. We're just having a go at checkers here. Join up. By the fire."

And he hurried back to the little table and the patiently waiting gathering and Jim and I awkwardly followed after him.

Friendly faces looked at us, without too much interest, and everybody in silence concentrated his gaze on the battered checker board on which only a few pieces remained, three white crowns, three black crowns, three white pieces and two black pieces.

With nothing but the humming of the stove and an occasional sniffle from one or other of the silent watchers, the board was intently stared at, while the storekeeper made several false starts, changed his mind, and then finally moved one of the black kings.

Everybody sighed and stared.

Opposite the storekeeper sat another elderly man, heavily coated and muffled. He instantly made a move with one of his white pieces.

An electric shock seemed to shake the room. Like a pouncing hawk, the storekeeper moved a king and in three more moves, the game was ended, the storekeeper the winner.

Everybody relaxed and there was a lot of laughing and going over of the plays.

"Anybody else?" cried the little storekeeper, gaily "It's cigars all round."

Jim looked at me and I at Jim.

"That's a sucker's move," murmured Jim. "That white piece."

"Sit in," I urged.

So Jim, after waiting a polite moment piped up and asked if strangers were admitted.

"Delighted," said the storekeeper.

"Is this game for money?" inquired Jim, jovially.

"No, sir," said the storekeeper. "Just cigars all round. That's the usual, hereabouts."

Jim sat down and took his overcoat off. I stood behind him. Jim is a good checker player. He can see three moves ahead. In a moment, all was tense once more in this quiet place of business. Only the stove hummed and a couple of friends sniffled. Jim started his well-known wedge play, right up the centre.

The storekeeper, with becoming caution, paused and studied the board keenly. He began several false moves but snatched his hand back. Jim continued his aggressive drive up the centre. The little shopkeeper continued his cautious, countrified game, nearly making moves, then pausing to reflect.

Jim, coming to the end of his wedge, startedup his rear guard.

With serpent-like suddenness, the little shopkeeper picked up one of his back men and jumped five of Jim's.

I saw it coming the instant he started, and loud exclamations and deep sniffles of delight came from the crowd and Jim, sitting violently back, saw the game over hardly before it had begun.

"Cigars all round," cried Jim, merrily, while the storekeeper jumped up and passed the box; five-centers, fortunately.

"Seven cigars," I counted aloud. "Make a note, Jim."

Jim relayed out his men and a second game started. This time, Jim took a little time with his famous centre wedge play. He too started backing and filling and reconsidering his play.

"Get the sides up," I said quietly.

Everybody looked at me, and three of them sniffled.

"Put two behind that forward one," I suggested a moment later.

Jim gave me an impatient bunt whith his elbow, and all the other watchers shifted their position a little and smiled briefly at me.

"Look out,"I cried, as Jim started to move one of his men.

"You don't talk , during checkers," said the shopkeeper, gently to me.

Jim moved. From a side position, the storekeeper shifted one checker, and there was Jim, cornered.

"Cigars all round," I cried heartily, and again the box of five-centers were passed and all the lads opened their overcoats and slipped the cigars inside. Three more visitors came noisily in the front door.

"May I?" I inquired, as Jim rose from the table.

"Certainly," cried the shopkeeper.

"You're sure I'm not holding up any of you gentlemen?" I inquired graciously, around the group of watchers, standing and leaning.

So we set out the pieces. No wedge game for me. I play what you might call random checkers. A sort of guerrilla warfare. Devil take the hindmost, as it were. By assuming an air of concentration and mystery and moving any old piece, I often come out as good as the next felow, and sometimes actually win.

At first, I had the shopkeeper buffaloed. In fact, I made two double jumps on him and could feel the tense air of the watchers around us. But then, quite suddenly, the storekeeper made a four jump and then got three kings out of nowhere and soon I was slaughtered.

"Cigars all round, nine cigars, make a note of it!" cried Jim, cheerily, and again they were passed and a new box opened. Two more strangers dropped in, stamping their feet.

"How about another game?" challenged the storekeeper.

"Okay," I replied heartily.

So we had another game, and the cigars went around once more and then Jimmie said it was 10 o'clock and our car would be ready. So we thanked everybody for a pleasant evening and got the car and soon left the lonely little village far behind.

As I stooped reverently to touch the fish in the basket, Mrs. Bushy gave another wild heave and derricked another trout out of the water.

Mrs I. Walton

"**O**H boy" cried Jimmy Frise, gripping the steering wheel, "it looks like fish to me."

"Slow down, slow down," I pleaded. "Let's look over the lay of the land as we go by."

"Look at that open stretch," breathed Jim. "Look at the log jams in the bends "

As we bumped slowly along the countryside road, to our left spread out semi-wild meadows in which meandered a trout stream amidst cedar thickets, willow clumps and alder.

"To think," exclaimed Jim, "that this stream has been here,

209

less than 80 miles from Toronto, all these years and we never even heard of it."

"Until Bill tipped us off," I pointed out. "We must give Bill credit. He knows where the trout streams are."

"I don't see anybody else fishing it," remarked Jim.

"Bill said that was the beauty of it," I reminded him. "Hardly anybody knows about it."

"The farm house," said Jim, "ought to be just past this next bit of brush."

So in expectant silence, we joggled and thudded over the narrow rutted road until we came in sight of the farm house which Bill had foretold us, and where we would find the elderly couple who owned this farm and this stream and from whom, for the payment of one dollar each we could obtain the privilege of fishing all day in as fine a stretch of trout stream as there is in Ontario.

The house had that white tidy look that farm houses have which are inhabited by elderly people whose children have all grown up and moved away, leaving the old folks to do all the pleasant things they have wanted to do all their lives. The fences repaired, the door yard tidy and trim, flower boxes on the window sills ready for the petunias of June and an old stiff dog waddling off the side porch to bark huskily and rather foolishly at our approach. No wreckage about the place, such as young people leave; no chores left undone by young men wanting to go to town; none of the bareness that comes to farm houses because of all the cares and all the jobs that call, indoors, outdoors, from the lowing barn and from the far acres.

"Jim," I said, "I like the look of this place."

And Jim steered in the short land and drew up alongside the pump.

On the side porch were two old rocking chairs. From the glass in the door a woman's face looked out in that curious fashion in which country people await your knock.

Jim and I got out, in all our fishing togs, and advanced, under the shrewd gaze of what appeared to be a motherly old lady with spectacles set half-way down her nose. And she was hurriedly tidying her hair.

She even let us rap on the door, and waited a decent interval before she opened; though she must have been standing three feet from it.

"Good-day, gentlemen," said she. And we both fell in love

with her, because of the way she looked over the top of her spectacles at us.

"Ma'am," said Jimmie, "a friend of ours sent us here to ask if we might have the privilege of the day's fishing on your trout stream."

"Aw," said the lady, whose name presently appeared to Mrs. Bushy, but which we changed for here before the night had fallen. "Aw, now boys, I hate to see you waste your time on our bit of water. In the olden days, we used to get great fishing here. But you know. Time and tide. Time and tide."

"Oh, don't you worry," cried Jim, " from what we've heard, we'll be satisfied. The charge, I understand, is a dollar."

"My husband," said Mrs. Bushy, "makes a rule to charge visitors a dollar each. It's just to keep people off, really. You'll never get a dollar's worth of trout out of that stream."

"We're only too glad to pay it," I cut in, wanting the dear old lady to look at me over her spectacles, too.

"Boys," said Mrs. Bushy, "my husband insists on a dollar because if we let everybody on the stream, there are always some who leave gates open and break down fences and build bonfires and leave trash around. But I take it you come from Toronto."

We admitted it, warily.

Two Nice Boys

"Then," said Mrs. Bushy, "Why not go another 20 or 30 miles further up, where there is some trout fishing? I just hate to take a dollar from two such nice boys. All the way from Toronto, why it's nearly 80 miles. And for another 20 miles or so, you could really get some fishing."

"Ma'am," said Jim, "we'd have to go a lot farther than 20 miles to get good trout fishing. It just so happens a friend told us about the sport he had here on your farm last year. Your farm is out of the way. It is off the beaten path. Sportsmen pass it by in the lure of more distant pastures."

"Boys," interrupted Mrs. Bushy, "take my advice. Don't waste your dollar."

"The greatest fishing in the world," I insisted, "is in the stream that is generally supposed to be fished out. The minute a trout stream gets the reputation of being fished out, the trout get a chance to grow in it."

"Listen, boys," said Mrs. Bushy. "I've lived here all my life. My father before me. We've fished that there stream for over 70 years. For the first few years, while we were clearing this land, that trout stream helped feed us.''

"It looks lovely," I said.

"It is lovely," said Mrs. Bushy. "Sit down, boys."

And she indicated the two rockers, but Jim and I made her sit down in one and I took the other and Jim sat on the step.

"It does look lovely," said Mrs. Bushy, "but of course there are no fish in it. Not many, anyway. Not worth a dollar."

"We'd like to spend the day on it, nevertheless," insisted Jimmie.

"When I was a little girl," said Mrs. Bushy, "my father used to go out and catch a wash boiler full of trout between here and that hill with the five elms on it. A wash boiler - full."

"What would you do with them?" asked Jim.

"We would have great feasts of them, breakfast, dinner and supper," said Mrs. Bushy, with a faraway look over her spectacles. "We would send them to old people of the neighbourhood, and sick people. And the minister. My father was given to fits and starts. He would fish all day from sunrise to sunset, and then never fish another worm for a year."

"You like fishing?" asked Jim.

"In fits and starts," said Mrs. Bushy. "I haven't fished for years."

"Have you ever made any great catches in your creek?" I inquired. "Any big fish?"

"I never could catch a wash boiler full." admitted Mrs. Bushy. "I've tried, but a couple of pails full is all I can remember. And never any big ones. My brother, when he was a boy, caught a fish of five pounds in that stream. At the log jams about half way to that hill, there with the five elms."

"Ma'am," said Jim, and we both rose to our feet, "despite what you say, we'd like to fish in your creek."

"Aw, boys," said Mrs. Bushy.

"You see," explained Jim, "it isn't trout a real fisherman is after. It's the fishing. The day in the open. On the stream. The expectation. The quiet. The peace and mystery. The hope."

"Hope is all you'll get," laughed Mrs. Bushy, over the top of her spectacles very twinkley. "I do wish you boys would go where there is trout."

"If you don't want us on the . . ." I submitted.

"No, no," cried the dear old lady leaping up. "My husband is away, but will be home before the day's out, so I'll simply have to abide by his rule. But I hate to take the dollar . . ."

But Jim and I had the dollar out of our pockets and handed them into her grudging soft hand and she hid them behind her without looking at them as if they were shameful.

"Come back," she said, "at noon, for lunch."

"Please," said Jim, "it is only two hours to noon, we'll just be getting started. And besides we have sandwiches . . ."

"Aw, you fishermen," said Mrs. Bushy.

"We'll see you on our way out," said Jim genially, "with a wash boiler full of trout."

"Stay for supper," said Mrs. Bushy, taking her hand from behind her, and revealing the crumpled and shameful dollars.

"No, no," we both cried. "We'll be late coming off the stream . . ."

"You'll be glad to quit before sundown," assured Mrs. Bushy, firmly. "I'll have something on the table for you here, whenever you come back."

Boxes of Knick-Knacks

So she stood and watched us unpack our gear, the rod cases, the fishing bags full of fly boxes and knick-knacks and shook her head when we pulled on our waders and set our rods up and over the top of her spectacles looked taken aback at so much preparation for so little in store.

"My dear boys," she said, when we were ready to haste down to the stream, "this is all so silly. But don't say I didn't warn you."

"Wait until we come back," we predicted confidently.

And down the land and out over a lumpy meadow we strode as hard as we could and came to the stream. A hurrying, gurgling, brim full and crystal clear stream it was, rising out of some miracle of springs back in the stony hills. A stream where trout should be, time nor tide. A stream it would be a pleasure to fish, if only in memory of the trout that once must have inhabited it.

"You fish up," said Jim, "and I'll fish down, and then we'll return and pass each other. Here's your sandwiches. I'll take mine. We won't waste time in meeting for lunch."

"Okay," I agreed, already whisking my line out, and bowing low, laid the first fly on a particular coiling bit of current, where a trout of 11 inches should be lurking.

With that fresh eagerness which, like the first plunge into water for a swimmer, is the best part of all, I fished up the

214

stream, slowly, patiently; casting a hundred times over each
likely pool and letting my flies dance down every ripple and
swim past all logs and embedded stumps along the margins. But
not a rise did I get; not a single flash or wink underwater of a
bright slashing worm of a trout. If there were trout in this
stream, they were sulky indeed.

Slow Disillusionment

Almost half a mile of wandering stream did I follow, in all de-
votion and unfailing expectation, until I came to the fence that
marked the end of the farm. In trout fishermen, disillusion is
slow in coming. In no other sport does hope die so hard. But
when it dies, it is apoplectic. It dies with a dunt. And when I
reached the boundary fence, disillusion fell on me like a weight,
and I climbed out and sat on the stream's bank to smoke. And a
brown thrasher, sensing my trouble, came and sang on a dead
tree his song, repeating each warble and each sardonic chuckle
once, as if glad to gloat on it, and I fell asleep a little, and woke
and began fishing down stream. But in all the smooth pools and
up against all the tangled and mysterious log jams, and in all the
coiling currents, I raised narry a fish. In time I passed the farmhouse and entered on the stretch. Jim had fished, and found
cress beds and sat down and had my sandwiches with fresh cress
for a salad to them. And fished on far down to where, with afternoon now well gone, I found Jim sitting at the foot of a tree
looking very dejected.

"Well," I said, climbing out to join him.

"How many?" said he dully.

"I haven't even seen a fish," I said. "Mrs. Bushy was an
honest woman. When will we ever learn to recognize truth when
it stands shining before us?"

"I got two," said Jim, turning out his basket where, in a mat
of mushy grass, two measly little seven-inch trout lay stiff and
stark.

"Well, thank goodness," I said, "at least there are a few
ghosts of trout left."

And we sat so for an hour, smoking and comparing the flies
we had used, Jim getting his two on a small black hackle and I
confessing to have tied on nine different patterns of fly in my effort to interest the fish.

"We may as well push off," said Jim. "A day like this is not
badly spent, though. I've had a swell day's practice."

"In fact," I agreed, "when you have to cast so hard for fish that won't rise, you get a lot better practice than when the fish are rising.''

We hoisted our bags and rods and walked slowly along the banks, through the thickets and followed the stream, stopping to admire the finest lays and marvelling that such water held no trout.

As banks, through the thickets and followed the stream, stopping to admire the finest lays and marvelling that such water held no trout.

As we came near the clearing that led out of the meadows to the farm, we heard a sound, and stopped to peer through the brush. Ahead of us someone was fishing.

We tiptoed. And in an open space, at the foot of a bank, stood Mrs. Bushy, armed with a pole cut from a birch sapling, dunking a great gob of worms which she threw with a splash into the open pool. She was standing out in full view on a log, and her white apron made a sign and a signal to all the trout in Christendom not to come near.

"The dear old soul," I murmured to Jim as we stood watching with amusement the spectacle. "Imagine her trying to catch trout in that white apron flapping in the wind, and her standing out in full view on that log.''

"Never mind, she's having fun,'' said Jim.

And at that instant Mrs. Bushy leaned forward, allowed her line to sink deeper with a look of great intensity on her, and then with a wild heave, she hoisted the pole and flung high over head and onto the sod far behind her a speckled trout of over one pound in weight.

"My gosh!'' gasped Jim.

So we broke into a trot and burst out of the bushes, to startle Mrs. Bushy, who was bent over trying to pick up the flapping trout thus unceremoniously bashed on to dry land.

"Great! great!'' we cried to her, dancing around.

And then we saw the basket. An ordinary fruit basket, in which lay, bright in death, nine beautiful trout, from a foot to 16 inches in length. The basket being almost full.

"Boys,'' said Mrs. Bushy. "I just thought in case you didn't have a catch, I would pick up a few for you.''

And she returned to the log, stepped out in full view, white apron and all, waved the pole terribly around, heaved the fat gob of worms with a terrific splash into the open pool, allowed it to drift down under the log jam and then, as I stooped reverently to touch the fish in the basket, gave another wild heave and derricked another pound and a half trout over her head, almost braining Jim with it as it hurtled through the air.

"There you are, boys," sighed Mrs. Bushy, happily. "Ten. That will be five each. Enough for a snack when you get home."

And Jim and I went furiously to work thinking the rise had begun; and we fished and we fished, with Mrs. Bushy following us and begging us to use her pole and worms, until dusk came and not a fish did we get, and then we walked all three up to the house.

Mr. Bushy was home and the dinner on. And we had one trout each, fried in butter; followed by cold roast beef and pickles and cabbage and old boiled potatoes, and plum pie and cheese and strong tea.

And we stayed until 10:30 o'clock, telling Mr. and Mrs. Bushy all about Izaak Walton and how he advocated all forms of fishing, scorning none; and then we gave Mrs. Bushy the new name of Mrs. Walton, Mrs. I. Walton, and then we drove out the side road and home, with three fine speckled trout each in our baskets, not counting Jim's two measlies.

Gregory Clark

Greg Clark is too famous and his life was too full to do him justice in this small space. Suffice it to say he was a man who had his priorities straight. He loved people, good talk, good fishing, good whiskey, and good tobacco. He won the Military Cross in World War I at Vimy Ridge yet never let the horror he experienced dull his appreciation of life. He knew everybody who was anybody in Canada and the English speaking world. He was a legend in his own time and one of the most widely read and best loved men in Canada. Hemmingway worked with him at the *Star* and said of Clark, "If he has a weakness it is having too much sense. He writes the best of anyone on the paper."*

He was born in Toronto in 1892 and started to work for the *Star* in 1911. From 1947 until 1975 he was associated first with the *Standard* in Montreal then with *Weekend Magazine*. He died in 1977.

Ernest Hemingway: A Life Story by Carlos Baker, Charles Scribner's Sons, New York.

James Frise

Jimmie Frise never had a formal drawing lesson in his life. He was born in 1891, grew up in rural Ontario and came to Toronto at the age of twenty determined to be a cartoonist. This ambition seemed unlikely to be fulfilled until, by one of those strokes of fortune of the kind that his fans would later come to expect of him, he submitted a cartoon to the *Toronto Star* depicting the editor milking a cow from the wrong side. This was a particularly apt comment on a controversy raging in the Letters to the Editor column, and he was hired immediately. Jimmie enlisted in the artillery in World War I and lost a part of his left hand at Vimy Ridge. In 1920 his cartoon series, "Life's Little Comedies" began to appear in the *Star*. The title changed to Birdseye Centre, it brought him national recognition and partnership with Greg Clark. He died in 1948.